Climate Change

What They Rarely Teach in College

The Milwaukee Sky (June 21, 2021)
The hottest day in Wisconsin history was July 13, 1936.
The temperature was 114 degrees Fahrenheit.[1]

Climate Change

What They Rarely Teach in College

STEPHEN EINHORN

ISBN: 979-8-218-13024-4 (Softcover)

Printed in the United States of America

1 2 3 4 5 6 7 8 9 10

Cover design by Vertz Marketing; Mequon, Wisconsin

To my grandchildren:
Rachel, Naomi, Mitchell, Emma,
Henry, Anna, and James

May you always search for the truth and not
simply accept the common narrative.

ACKNOWLEDGMENTS

I must first thank my wife, Nancy, for her advice, suggestions, and edits, which provided good judgment, wisdom, and realism. Also,

- Jacky Christiansen, Katy Almond, Jacob DeZarn, and Alvin Vitangcol—my colleagues, who provided significant computer skills and support for this book.

- David Hoyt, James Taylor, Anthony Watts, and especially Joe and Diane Bast of The Heartland Institute, who provided significant support and encouraged me to complete this challenging project.

- Sam Nelson (Professor of Communications at Cornell University) for allowing a debate on climate change in a liberal university where this subject is considered settled science.

- Greg Wrightstone, my mentor, who multiplied my knowledge and provided the basis for this book.

- OmniBios Inc., for professionalizing many aspects of my book.

TABLE OF CONTENTS

TABLE OF FIGURES

Preface

In the contentious debate over climate change, two areas of general agreement stand out: (1) The average surface temperature on Earth has been slowly rising since the mid-nineteenth century by about 1°C, and (2) The burning of fossil fuels has contributed to a rise of about 1 part in 10,000 in atmospheric carbon dioxide (CO_2). Beyond these two areas of agreement are many unsettled questions:

- Are global temperatures rising at a significant rate?
- How big a role does CO_2 play in the climate?
- Should we be concerned about rising sea levels?
- Is climate change causing more hurricanes, tornadoes, and forest fires?
- Are coral reefs dying because of acidification?
- Will polar bears disappear, and will there be an increase in animal extinctions?
- How easy or difficult would it be to replace fossil fuels with alternative energy sources?
- What will be the impact of climate change in the future?

Isn't it best to address these sensitive topics without censorship or name-calling? I hope so. I am not a meteorologist, but I am a long-time student of global warming and climate change. My formal education consists of a BA in Chemistry from Cornell University, an MS in Polymeric Materials (that is, big molecules) from Brooklyn Polytechnic Institute, and attending Wharton Graduate School. I've also worked for 40 years in the chemical industry and 15 years in venture capital.

My goal in writing this book is to provide the statements, beliefs, and claims of both sides of the climate change debate accompanied by historical data and empirical science with an objective evaluation of each side's predictions. I am confident that after reading this material, you will be able to form your own opinion, whether or not you agree with the information presented. In particular, I hope that more of our educational institutions, which too often walk with the most Activist views on climate change, will allow a diversity of ideas to be considered and that the students and professors who read this book gain confidence that the Earth's climate change is a joy to behold.

I have tried to make a balanced presentation of the opinions, facts, and science from both sides on the topics of global warming and climate change. I can't help it, but the facts and so-called "science" of the Activists are almost always wrong! Still, I have tried to avoid most political issues and concentrate on empirical and scientific facts. I have presented the science without scientific jargon by writing in plain English. Much of the data I report comes from U.S. government agencies. The book has hundreds of endnotes so the reader can search the original citation and form an opinion of its validity.

You will note that this book includes significant repetition, particularly relating to major issues such as sea-level rise, major climatic events, and animal extinctions. This repetition is intentional and is aimed at making later sections of the book self-contained. Feel free to skip the repetition if you choose.

Although a number of the charts and supporting documents relate to global conditions, this book generally focuses on U.S. statistics. To some extent, this is because, in general, U.S. statistics are more accurate or more readily available.

Since "who funded you" seems to be one of the most favored questions of the day, I can report that I have not received any money from any companies or interest groups to write, produce, or sell this book. However, if any major oil company, Climate Activist, or Climate Realist chooses to compensate me, the money will be cheerfully accepted.

Finally, let me recommend that when a man approaches a woman whom he would like to meet, he should start the conversation by talking about global warming.

It's a real ice breaker.

Stephen Einhorn
June 15, 2022

Chapter 1
Introduction to the Climate Debate

"No one is educated who knows only one side of an argument."
(John Stuart Mill)

The author explains the difference between Climate Activists and Climate Realists; why the 97% consensus is a myth; what you really want to know about greenhouse gases and global warming; news about the "Ideal Temperature" for humans; and the relative dangers of cold or hot weather.

Climate Activists versus Climate Realists

The climate change debate is generally divided into two opposing camps, which I will call Climate Activists (or Climate Crisis people) and Climate Realists (or Climate Accepters). I will refer to these two opposing climate groups as the Activists and the Realists. Naturally, people often support intermediate positions which fall between these two opposites.

Climate Activists tell us that climate change requires immediate action, which specifically means ending or dramatically reducing the use of fossil fuels (oil, gas, coal). I call them Activists not to disrespect them but because they sound the alarm from the rooftops and believe that climate change is not only a crisis but will shortly become a catastrophe if we do not change our ways.

Climate Realists say climate change is not a crisis. They base their decisions on actual historical data for such things as sea-level rise and animal extinctions and base their climate change projections on long-term climate trends. They view climate change as primarily a continuation of the past. They weigh both the costs and benefits of climate-related decisions, which they say Activists overlook.

Let me make it clear. I believe Activists are just as good people as Realists. I believe most Activists truly believe science supports their positions, just as Realists believe science supports theirs. Although both sides have confidence in those who support their views, the great majority of social media, general media, government workers, and university professors support the Activists. There are some on both sides who are dishonest. However, I believe there are more Activists than Realists that fit into this category because the science is almost entirely on the side of the Realists.

One reason it's difficult to obtain a balanced picture of climate change is that we have read and been told so many times that global warming is the "existential threat of our age" and that "the science is settled." These strong statements are supported by even stronger statements filled with emotion. For example, Greta Thunberg, the young Swedish Activist, tells us, "Around the year 2030…we will set off an irreversible chain reaction beyond our control that will most likely lead to catastrophe." As I will explain later, there is virtually no scientific support for this statement, but the message is still effective because her audience is large and her delivery is exceptional. The result is that millions of children (and many adults) are unjustifiably scared.

Even the staunchest Activists recognize there are some scientists who disagree with them. For your benefit, I will identify some of the leading Realist scientists in this book. And yet, the media and many Activist scientists refer to themselves as "scientists" and their adversaries as "science deniers" or "climate deniers"[2] as if an astrophysicist or meteorologist who disagrees with them is not a scientist and is a proponent of anti-science. The name-calling by Activists distracts us from objectively participating in the climate change debate.

The 97% Consensus Myth

Climate Activists claim that there is a "97% scientific consensus" that global warming and climate change are major issues and should be addressed immediately. Claiming "scientific consensus" is one of their basic arguments. A problem with the consensus argument was addressed by Albert Einstein when he wrote, "Genius abhors consensus because when consensus is reached, thinking stops."[3]

So where did this claim of 97% consensus of human responsibility for significant global warming and cataclysmic climate change come from? Although it was not the first article to claim that such a consensus existed,[4] the most important source was a 2013 article by John Cook and 12 others titled *Quantifying the Consensus on Anthropogenic Global Warming in the Scientific Community*.[5] Cook, with a dozen volunteers, examined almost 12,000 climate abstracts from 1991-2011 matching the topics "global climate change" or "global warming." Cook concluded that 97% of the abstracts[6] endorsed the consensus that humans are causing significant global warming. By 2016, Cook's paper had been downloaded 500,000 times, the most of any climate change paper.[7]

Cook's group, *Skeptical Science*, tells us in its *Consensus Project* that "97% of climate papers stating a position on human-caused global warming agree: "Global warming is happening and we are the cause."[8] But Cook's conclusion is misleading because the meaning of "We are the cause" can only be understood as either (1) humans are the only cause or (2) they are the primary cause of significant global warming. That was the actual conclusion of only about 1% of these almost 12,000 articles.

Of the articles Cook examined, 66% expressed no opinion on whether or not human activities cause or even contribute to global warming. Cook simply ignored those articles, which should be classified as "undecided" and therefore not evidence of consensus.

Of the 34% that expressed an opinion, 33% suggested, assumed, or implied that significant global warming was to some degree (major or trivial) caused by humans, and 1% wrote there was no connection. Cook divided 33% by 34% and derived his 97% consensus, which is a remarkable claim since fewer than 100 of the almost 12,000 articles claimed humans are *primarily* responsible for significant global warming.[9]

Contradicting Cook's claims, large surveys, literature reviews, and petition projects have been undertaken, revealing thousands of scientists who disagree with the alleged "consensus." For example, a George Mason University survey of 4,000 American Meteorological Society members found that only 18% believed man could significantly alter the climate.[10]

As Michael Crichton wrote, "There is no such thing as consensus science. If it is consensus, it is not science. If it is science, it is not consensus. Period!"[11] The Activists rarely point out that many world-leading scientists have rejected the consensus argument, including Edward Teller, one of American history's leading scientists, and the following leading scientists who dropped out of the U.N. Intergovernmental Panel on Climate Change (IPCC) to protest the Activists' views: **Frederick Seitz**, former president of both the National Academy of Sciences and Rockefeller University; **Christopher Landsea**, the Science and Operations Officer at the National Hurricane Center; **Richard S. Lindzen,** Professor of Meteorology at MIT; **Richard Tol**, professor of climate change at the Vrije Universiteit Amsterdam; **Robert Stavins,** Harvard professor and Director of Harvard Project on Climate Agreements.[12] All of these leading scientists are called "Climate Deniers" by the Activists.

Historically, the largest group of scientists who disagreed with the 97% consensus were the 31,000 scientists who signed the Oregon Petition.[13] David Burton, one of the signers, wrote: "I and 31,486 other American scientists… really did sign the Oregon Petition. It is completely legitimate and has far more signers than any of the climate activists' petitions."[14] Since there were over 30,000 scientists who signed the Oregon Petition, the Activists would need to find 1,000,000 scientists to reasonably conclude a 97% consensus exists. Good luck!

The Oregon Petition urged the U.S. government to reject the global warming Kyoto Protocol of 1997, which committed 192 countries to reduce their greenhouse emissions.[15] Here is what they signed:

> There is no convincing scientific evidence that human release of carbon dioxide, methane, or other greenhouse gases is causing or will, in the foreseeable future, cause catastrophic heating of the Earth's atmosphere and disruption of the Earth's climate. Moreover, there is substantial scientific evidence that increases in atmospheric carbon dioxide produce many beneficial effects upon the natural plant and animal environments of the Earth.[16]

Greenhouse Gases

When the sun's rays strike the Earth's surface, some are reflected back into the atmosphere, where they excite certain gases. These gases, called greenhouse gases, radiate heat in all directions, including back to the Earth, where they provide warmth. Carbon dioxide (CO_2) is one such gas. Without greenhouse gases, the Earth's temperature would be below freezing, and the planet would be uninhabitable.

There is agreement among scientists that atmospheric CO_2 levels are increasing. During the past 60 years, the Mauna Loa Observatory in Hawaii has recorded an increase of about 1 part in 10,000 or 100 parts per million (ppm).[17]

Figure 1: 1 Part in 10,000 (100 parts/million) Increase over 60 Years in Atmospheric CO2

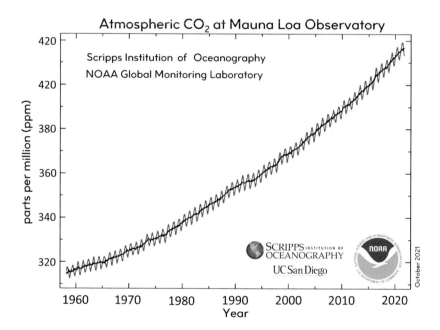

Activists make a big deal of the fact that our world has not seen current levels of atmospheric CO_2 at 400 ppm for several hundred thousand years, which is true.[18] Perhaps the rise in atmospheric CO_2 levels by 1 part in 10,000 is no more relevant than the fact that when dinosaurs were thriving

140 million years ago, the atmosphere contained five times more CO_2.[19] To our knowledge, the dinosaurs were quite happy at this level of CO_2, and although I have researched this issue, I have been unable to find any proof that excessive atmospheric CO_2 was a concern for them or injured their health.

In his book, *An Inconvenient Truth,* Al Gore tells us, "Of all the greenhouse gases, CO_2 usually gets top billing because it accounts for 80% of total greenhouse gas emissions."[20] My hope is that Gore's estimate of 80% was just a typo because that statement is totally false since 80% is 20 times the actual concentration of CO_2 in the atmosphere.

Gore's book never mentions that water vapor is by far the largest and most significant greenhouse gas. Water vapor accounts for about 95% of all greenhouse gases in the atmosphere (by volume) and about 60% of its warming effect.[21] Without water vapor acting as a greenhouse gas, the Earth would be frozen. However, the media, the EPA, and other U.S. government agencies[22] rarely mention water vapor when discussing climate change. Instead, they attack CO_2, a minor gas that constitutes just 0.04% of the atmosphere (by volume) and 3.6% of atmospheric greenhouse gases.

Figure 2: Percentage of Atmospheric Greenhouse Gases[23]

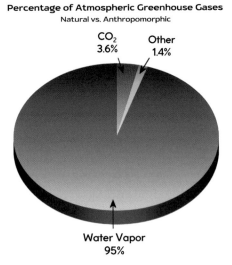

Percentage of Atmospheric Greenhouse Gases
Natural vs. Anthropomorphic

CO_2
3.6%

Other
1.4%

Water Vapor
95%

CO_2 gets a bad rap![24] CO_2 is an organic, odorless, and colorless gas.[25] The CO_2 in the air is 100% safe. It is not a health hazard, and there is no evidence that it will cause any sickness or death. This was true yesterday and today and will almost certainly be true tomorrow and in 12, 50, or 100 years.[26] The EPA has determined that CO_2 is safe at even 10 times its current concentration in the air[27] and that the increase in CO_2 has had no ill health effect on anyone.[28]

Humans have long enjoyed the advantages of a symbiotic relationship with plants and trees. We release CO_2 whenever we exhale, burn fossil fuels, make cement, or in some cases, change land use. Plants use their photosynthesis talents to provide us with oxygen. The more CO_2 we create, the more plants flourish. It becomes easier for the pores of plants, called stomata, to open and add water to their leaves. Human CO_2 improves plant growth and crop yields, creating a widely reported "Greening of the Earth."[29] Increasing CO_2 beyond current levels even by 300 ppm would likely increase average plant growth by more than 40%.[30]

Carbon dioxide is important. It provides the sparkle in soda, beer, and other carbonated beverages,[31] makes dough rise, makes fire extinguishers effective, and is the composition of dry ice, one of the world's most effective coolants.

Many scientists, such as Dr. Willie Soon, an astrophysicist and researcher at the Harvard-Smithsonian Center for Astrophysics, believe increases in atmospheric CO_2, including that caused by the burning of fossil fuels, have had little or no measurable effect on the global climate or average surface temperature.[32] But Dr. Soon, like so many other qualified scientists who dissent from the alleged "consensus," is dismissed by the media as "not part of the scientific community."[33]

Perhaps you have asked yourself, what would happen to the Earth's temperature if we reduced our CO_2 output substantially? The Activists demand that we reduce our CO_2 output, or our current climate will be destroyed. This is the basis of the Paris Agreement, which outlines steps necessary to reduce our carbon footprint.

But if we look at recent history, we have proof that *virtually nothing will happen* if we seriously reduce our use of fossil fuels. How do we know? We all know that during the COVID-19 global pandemic air flights, car driving, and industrial output significantly reduced our use of fossil fuels[34], and there was no noticeable effect on global temperatures.[35] The Center for International Climate Research (CICR) estimated in 2020 that "the enormous reduction in CO_2 generation reduced global temperatures by less than one five-hundredth of a degree Fahrenheit"[36] (1/500th of 1 degree = .002°F). In other words - virtually nothing.

Global Warming

Let's move on to global temperatures and start where there is the most agreement: In the last 140 years, the average global temperature has increased by about 1 degree Celsius (1°C),[37] as shown below.

Figure 3: Global Average Temperature, 1880 - 2020[38]

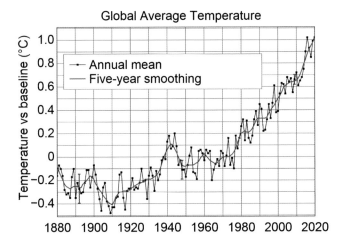

This chart may look like there has been a sharp increase in temperature, but isn't it remarkable that the average temperature of the Earth has changed only 1 degree in 140 years? How blessed we are to have so minimal a climate change over such a long period! The Earth's temperature has been warming for thousands of years. During the most recent glacial period, the "Ice Age," the ice grew to more than 12,000 feet thick as sheets spread across Canada, Scandinavia, Russia, and South America.[39] The Ice Age, about 18,000 years ago, was obviously before human CO_2 emissions could possibly have been a factor.

Since the Earth is gradually warming, you would expect the 10 warmest years would be in the recent past. Global satellite observations for the entire Earth for the 10 warmest years are shown below.[40]

Figure 4: 2016 was the Warmest Recent Year

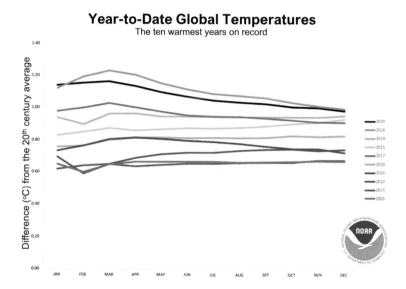

As you can see in Figure 4 above, especially if you have good eyesight, the range of temperature differences between the 10 warmest years is minimal, about ½ degree. As an individual, it is unlikely that you could distinguish the difference between the average temperature on Earth between the warmest and coldest years in that chart. If you disagree with me, go to your room's thermostat and make it warmer by 1 degree and see if you can tell the difference. Or better still, go to your car with a friend and have your friend increase or decrease the temperature by one degree and see if you can correctly identify the difference. I doubt that you can.

With such a small increase in temperature (1°C) over 140 years, you would expect that the warmest days for many cities would not be within the last few years. Sure enough, New York City reached its hottest day in 1936[41] and Miami in 1985.[42] Some have been in more recent years, like Houston in 2012[43] and San Francisco in 2000.[44] [45] A few cities, like Seattle, reached their peak temperature in 2021, but these are a minority.[46]

Also, there have been periods when there has been no increase in temperature. This is precisely the recent case for the last 5 years (2017-2021). As verified in Figure 5 below, the Earth has been cooler during the past 5 years.[47] This is a major fact that is rarely disclosed in the media, social media, or your local newspaper. Since the Activists claim global warming is "the existential threat of our time," why do you think they have kept the recent cooler weather a secret? Do you think it is an accident that most Americans don't know that it has been cooler for 5 years?

Figure 5: There Has Been No Global Warming for Five Years[48]

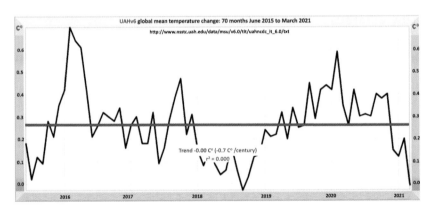

Global "Warming" 1944 – 1976

Let's start with predictions of climate change based on global warming. It is well established that "It was the post-war industrialization (1945-1975) that caused the rapid rise in global CO_2 emissions,"[49] and yet, during this time, the Earth was in a cooling phase.[50] Between 1944 and 1976, the Earth had temperatures decline while CO_2 growth was significant.[51]

**Figure 6: CO_2 Increases and Temperature Decreases
1944-1976**

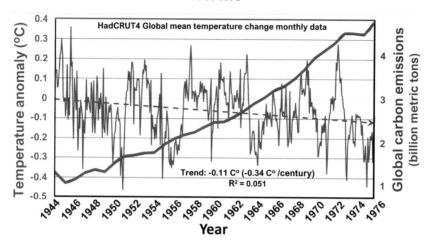

What the above chart makes clear is that for 32 years, between 1944 and 1976, CO_2 did not cause any global warming. There were significant increases in atmospheric CO_2 but NOT any increase in world temperatures. In the 1970s, the prevailing belief was that the Earth was sentenced to *major global cooling.* Because much of this history has been scrubbed from the internet, Google provides very limited information about which experts predicted a global cooling crisis at that time. Paul Ehrlich, a Professor at Stanford and author of *The Population Bomb,* was a significant proponent of global cooling,[52] but the internet provides little information about his global cooling belief. In 1958, author Betty Friedan[53] wrote a *Harper's Bazaar* article titled *The Coming Ice Age* about two university scientists, Ewing and Donn, and concluded, "If they are right, the world is now heading into another Ice Age. It will come not as a sudden catastrophe, but as the inevitable culmination of a process that has already begun in northern oceans."

The Ideal Temperature for Humans is___?

One reason some Activists tell us we cannot allow even a 1 degree increase from current temperatures is because there is an "ideal" temperature for humans. Among different Activist experts, there seems to be disagreement on what that "ideal" temperature is. Here are 3 differing opinions: Europe

52°F (11°C),[54] Sidney, Australia 71°F (22°C),[55] and the world 55°F (13°C).[56] Texas Tech climate scientist Katharine Hayhoe claims to have solved this dilemma by stating the best temperature for us all is what we have had in the past. As she tells us, "There is no one perfect temperature for the Earth, but there is for us humans, and that's the temperature we've had over the last few thousands of years."[57]

Let's examine the statement that the perfect temperature is what "we've had over the last few thousand years," In Alaska, the average low temperature in February is -10°F (-3°C).[58] In Burkina Faso, Africa, the best time to visit is November, when the average high temperature is 94°F.[59] How "ideal" for you are these temperatures in Alaska and Burkina Faso? Lord Christopher Monckton, a British statistician and science writer, commented, "No one knows what the optimal temperature is for a human being."[60] Doesn't that seem reasonable?

A headline in the *Milwaukee Journal Sentinel* in 2020 proclaimed, "Billions may face 'unlivable' heat in 50 years."[61] The article described a paper by Marten Scheffer, Tim Lenton, and a team of archaeologists, ecologists, and climate scientists, which claimed that by 2070 up to 3 billion people would likely have to move to climates with lower temperatures.[62] Scheffer and Lenton claimed, "These brutally hot climate [one degree warmer] conditions will spread to about 20% of the Earth's land area. Large areas of the planet would heat to barely survivable levels," and "3.5 billion people (roughly 30% of the projected global population) would have to move to other areas if the global population were to stay distributed relative to temperature the same way it has been for the past millennia."

These conclusions contradict past human behavior. Consider the case of Burkina Faso, a small land-locked country in Western Africa, briefly mentioned above, with the distinction of being the warmest country in the world. The average annual daily low temperature in Burkina Faso is 73°F, and the average high is 93°F.[63]

Figure 7: Burkina Faso, the Warmest Country on Earth

Based on the Scheffer and Lenton article, one would expect the population of Burkina Faso would have fallen since 1950, when it was 4 million, as its inhabitants moved away from the unbearable heat. Actually, the population has *increased* to 20 million.[64] Burkina Faso is not the only warm country that has grown rapidly during the past 70 years. The population of Africa, the warmest continent, has grown by more than 1 billion people since 1950 and now exceeds 1.3 billion.[65]

Katharine Hayhoe, mentioned above and one of the leading Climate Activists, told us these high temperatures will result in a decrease of at least 10% GDP,[66] which contradicts the *reality* in Burkina Faso, where GDP has *grown* by 3% to 6% yearly. To get a better grip on reality, Hayhoe could probably benefit from a trip to Burkina Faso, a country that has probably never seen one day where the temperature was between 52°F and 59°F and the claimed "optimal human climate niche."

When one compares Africa and Europe, the results also contradict the "climate niche" theory. Africa, the warmest continent, has a population of more than 1 billion, which is four times greater than it was 40 years ago. Europe, with colder average temperatures,[67] has had static populations of 700 million. Italy, the only major European country with average temperatures between 52°F and 59°F (the "optimal human climate niche"), has a lower GDP than England, Germany, or France. This is contrary to the "ideal" temperature thesis.

Based on their belief in global warming and their computer models, Climate Activists such as Scheffer and Lenton would likely predict that Americans would be moving from Florida (average temperature 71°F) to places within the "ideal climate niche" like New York (average temperature 54°F).[68] But the migration has been in the opposite direction. During the past 7 years, 300,000 New Yorkers moved to Florida.[69] We can probably agree that taxes and air-conditioning may be factors that prompted this. But this simply reinforces the point that average temperature is a minor factor in people's decisions about where to live.

An April 2020 *Fortune* magazine article by Brian O'Keefe, titled *A Planet in Crisis,* reads, "In the U.S., the optimal temperature at which economic performance peaks is 55°F." This figure came from peer-reviewed articles by researchers at Stanford University and Berkeley in California. Since the average temperature in the United States is currently only 53°F,[70] these climate experts appear unable to make up their minds: On the one hand, they tell us that an increase of 2°F will bring us to their ideal temperature (55°F) and will make the U.S. richer and healthier; but we are told daily that a 2°F increase is the Paris Agreement disaster scenario which will make us poorer, sicker, and produce a catastrophic climate. Aren't we both rooting for their more optimistic scenario?

Deaths Due to Temperature Extremes

Climate Activists claim exposure to higher temperatures will cause more people to die. This ignores the fact that the additional warmth that has occurred so far took place at night and in winter when the Earth is cooler.[71] Most studies of deaths from extreme temperatures conclude that more people die from cold than heat, so the net effect of global warming should be fewer lives lost to extreme temperatures. Three studies concluded that (1) Over 8% of all deaths were due to abnormally cold conditions and less than 1% to heat, which means that a 1°C global warming would save 166,000 lives each year;[72] (2) If significant global warming were to occur, the number of deaths attributed to cold weather in the European Union would fall by 100,000;[73] (3) That only 1 in 250 deaths were related to heat, but 1 in 20 deaths were related to cold.[74]

Figure 8: Deaths Caused by Cold vs. Heat

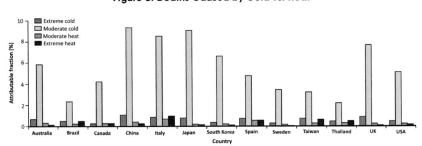

Nevertheless, the article on this topic that received the most attention in 2021 was by Ana Vicedo-Cabrera of the University of Bern in Switzerland, who concluded that, on average, 10,000 people in about 700 cities die every year because of global warming.[75][76] I decided to ask Vicedo-Cabrera how she could conclude that warmer weather is more significant than cold weather without doing a study that included cold weather. Therefore, I wrote her in June 2021 requesting her thoughts on deaths caused by cold weather.[77] Should she choose to reply, I plan to send her the studies above, which prove that cold weather is far more dangerous to humans than warm weather.

Chapter 1 Quiz

	True	False
1. There is significant disagreement between Climate Activists and Realists, but Activists are almost always respectful of Climate Realists.		
2. John Cook's 2013 paper proved that 97% of climate scientists believe significant global warming is happening and that human activity is causing it.		
3. Al Gore, in his movie and book, *An Inconvenient Truth,* acknowledged that water vapor is by far the most significant greenhouse gas.		
4. High levels of CO_2 are dangerous to human health and do not benefit trees and vegetation.		
5. A temperature increase of 2°C from pre-industrial times will cause mass human migration and terminate economic growth.		
6. Human populations grow fastest and are more prosperous in parts of the world where the average surface temperature is between 52°F and 59°F.		
7. During the past five years, large increases in CO_2 emissions caused large increases in worldwide average temperatures.		
8. Temperatures rose between 1944-1976 when CO_2 emission increases were large.		
9. More people die from being too warm than from being too cold.		

The answers to all of the questions are False. Here's why:

1. Activists often mock realists and call them Luddites, Flat Earth People, Climate Deniers, and Science Deniers. Climate Realists have lost academic positions and been denied access to scholarly journals.

2. John Cook and his assistants read the abstracts of 12,000 scientific papers and found that less than 1% said significant global warming was primarily caused by human activity.

3. Al Gore, in his movie and book, *An Inconvenient Truth,* never once mentioned that water vapor, not carbon dioxide, is by far the most abundant greenhouse gas.

4. CO_2 is a colorless and odorless gas whose presence in the air has no negative effect on humans and is essential for all plant life.

5. Dire predictions of mass migration to cooler climates and economic losses due to climate change have not been validated by real-world data or experience.

6. Climate actually plays a very small role in where people choose to live and work. Many countries outside the supposed "optimal climate niche," including England, Germany, and France, do better economically than those within the niche, such as Italy.

7. During the past 5 years, historically large increases in atmospheric CO_2 levels were accompanied by no increase in the worldwide average surface temperature.

8. Temperatures decreased between 1944 and 1976 despite rapidly increasing atmospheric CO_2.

9. Most scientific studies conclude that more people have died due to extreme cold weather than extreme warm weather.

FAKE NEWS: In 2020, at the annual meeting of the International Association of Greenhouse Gas Molecules (IAGGM), the Global Warming (GW) Subcommittee meeting went poorly. As you probably expected, this was going to be a contentious meeting with serious disputes between the Water Vapor molecules and the Carbon Dioxide molecules. The Carbon Dioxide molecules, with only 40 delegates, were totally dominated by the 940 Water Vapor delegates. The Carbon Dioxide molecules complained that they were an oppressed minority and that there was an international effort to suppress Carbon Dioxide molecules. The Carbon Dioxide molecules developed a new strategy of going to their supporters, namely the trees, plants, vegetables, and fruits, to support their demands for equity and improved molecular diversity. It is rumored that a very small minority of Methane Molecules will support the Carbon Dioxide molecules in this effort.

Summary

We should not fear, worry, or feel guilty about Global Warming or Climate Change because:

- The average temperature on Earth has increased by one degree in 100 years. The last 5 years have been cooler and, based on recent empirical history, there is no indication that the Earth will have any meaningful temperature increase in the future.

- The greenhouse gases prevent us from freezing. Carbon dioxide is a minimal player, and water vapor is the major greenhouse gas. But the Activists, led by Al Gore, who wrote *An Inconvenient Truth*, the world's most influential environmental book, tend not to mention this fact.

- There is no consensus that humans have a major problem with Global Warming and Climate Change.

- Consensus is not science, and science is not consensus.

Chapter 2
Sea Levels

"We are being hit with a massive wave of
misinformation about climate change."
(John Cook)

The author explains that there has been a slow rise of sea levels with virtually no increase in the rate for 100 years; that worldwide sea levels are rising at about 1 foot per century; that any changes in ice levels in Antarctica or other glacial areas have caused minimal, if any, acceleration in sea level rise at any major city or any identified location in the world; that the computer projections of the Activists are guided by bias and their conclusions differ from nature; that claims of the Activists that sea levels will rise in the near future by 20 feet have no scientific basis and there is no rational justification for the reader to worry about the rise of the seas.

The Importance of Sea Levels

This chapter concentrates solely on the rise in sea levels, and I really would appreciate it if you read it completely. Let me explain why: Everyone would agree that if sea levels were to rise significantly, say 20 feet in the near future, all of the world's great seacoast cities, including New York, Calcutta, Buenos Aires, Mumbai, Los Angeles, Shanghai, and Tokyo would likely suffer from catastrophic climate change. Millions of people would abandon their flooded homes and businesses, move to higher ground, lose their livelihoods, and trillions of dollars would be required to address this disaster while terror, fear, and unrest would permeate humanity. Of all the potential climate crises identified by the Activists, this is the one that frightens a majority of us the most.

Therefore, it is important to recognize that this scenario, based almost entirely on junk science, is exactly what the Climate Activists are teaching us. For example, in *An Inconvenient Truth* (2006), history's most successful movie on global warming and climate change, which had an audience of 7 million,[78][79] Al Gore tells us that, due to global warming, melting ice could release enough water to **cause a 20-foot rise in sea level "in the near future."**[80] Unfortunately, the mass media and the liberal universities promoted and supported this nonsensical fear: For example, the Associated Press reported that "(all of the) climate scientists (they contacted) who had seen the movie or read the book said that Gore accurately conveyed the science, with few errors."[81] William Schlesinger, Dean of the Environmental School at Duke University, said, "(Gore) got all of the important material and got it right."[82]

Let's take 15 years (2006-2021) as a reasonable time frame for Gore's "the near future" and examine how accurate Gore's prediction has been. Most Americans believe that U.S. government (NASA) satellites provide accurate data on sea levels. NASA's scientific study, as shown below, reveals that the rise in sea levels during the last 30 years has been a consistent 3.4 millimeters (mm) per year, or about one inch every 8 years.

**Figure 9: U.S. Government Data on World Sea Level Rise:
3.4 mm/year= 1 inch in 8 years = one foot in 100 years**

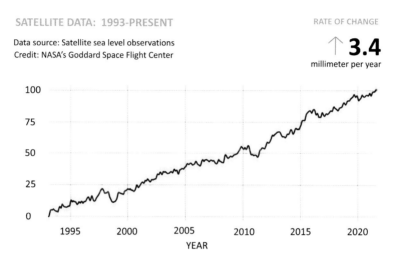

SATELLITE DATA: 1993-PRESENT

Data source: Satellite sea level observations
Credit: NASA's Goddard Space Flight Center

RATE OF CHANGE

↑ **3.4**
millimeter per year

If we compare NASA's scientific satellite studies with Gore's 2006 prediction, we see *Gore was wrong by a factor of 100!*

Figure 10: Sea Level Rise (15 years)

Source of Information	Comparison
U.S. Government (NASA) – Actual	2 inches
Al Gore, *An Inconvenient Truth* - Prediction	20 feet

If the sea level continues to rise at its historic pace, Gore's 20 feet projection will be correct in about 2000 years. Should we panic now?

In his book, *An Inconvenient Truth*, Gore reminds us of a famous quip by Mark Twain, "It ain't what you don't know that gets you into trouble; it is what you know for sure that just ain't so."[83] His "20 feet" warning of sea level rise is a perfect example of where Mark Twain would recommend that Gore should look in the mirror! Gore was not the first or the only one to falsely predict enormous sea level rises. A multitude of poor predictions has come from the U.N. through its IPCC group and other Climate Activists for many years.

- In 1989, the U.N. predicted that "Entire nations could be wiped off the face of the Earth by rising sea levels if global warming is not reversed by the year 2000."[84]

- Between 1989 and 1990, Paul Ehrlich, a leading Activist, warned that "We'll be in rising waters with no ark in sight"; that "within a century, the sea level will rise 10-20 feet."[85]

- In 2005, Dr. James Bogardi at the U.N. University in Bonn predicted that there would be 50 million refugees by 2010 due to rising sea levels and shrinking freshwater supplies. This would be a "new category of refugees" who were "fleeing untenable environmental conditions" due to climate change. [86]

- Hans van Ginkel, U.N. Under-Secretary General, told us that "As many as 100 million people" would be affected and that we needed an immediate "Intergovernmental panel on environmental degradation ... to assess the situation."[87] Despite the historical realities, the U.N. IPCC predicts that the sea level will rise by four times the current rate, to 15 mm/year by 2100.[88]

- Rising seas could result in 2 billion refugees, and those who once lived on coastlines will face displacement and resettlement bottlenecks as they seek habitable places inland (The Cornell Chronicle 2017).[89]

Let me ask you, how many millions of people do you think are frightened and upset when they are told by "climate experts" that entire nations could be "wiped off the face of the Earth" or that "100 million people" would become "environmental refugees?" Even though none of this has happened, and there are no current or historic refugees from rising seas, the Activists continue to make similar predictions of impending catastrophes. And for some reason, many otherwise thoughtful and intelligent people continue to take them seriously.

The Reality of Sea Level Rise

The U.S. Geological Survey tells us that sea levels began to rise over 15,000 years ago, but the rate of increase has been much slower during the past 7,000 years.[90]

Figure 11:[91] **The Sea Level Has Risen For 15,000 Years**

20,000 years of sea level rising...

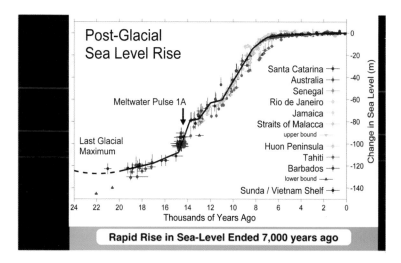

We know that the global sea level has risen at the *constant rate of 1 inch every 8 years* since around 1880.[92] [93] [94] [95] The exact rise varies with location, but in each location, the sea level has risen consistently almost every year.[96] This is confirmed by measurements at the world's seven largest shoreline cities. Some, like Los Angeles and Mumbai, have risen 1 mm/year; others, like Calcutta and Tokyo, have risen 4 mm/year; and all have risen at an almost constant rate.[97]

Figure 12: The World's Largest Cities by the Sea
All increases have been almost constant for the
past 100 years

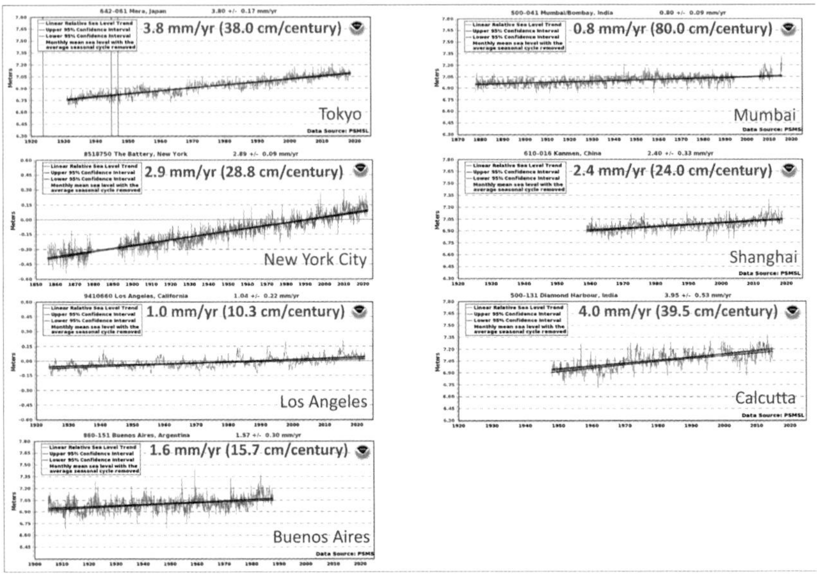

In some places, there has been almost no rise, and in other places, the sea levels are actually falling. For example, in Sydney, Australia, during the past 140 years, the sea level has risen less than 4 inches, and in Stockholm, Sweden, the sea level has constantly been falling at almost 4 mm/per year.[98, 99]

Sea Level Rise in the U.S.

If you are convinced that the rise in sea levels is nothing to worry about, feel free to skip to the next chapter. However, if you do, let me warn you that you will miss my exciting explanation of what is really happening in Miami.

Earlier, you saw that the sea level rise in New York City and Los Angeles, the two largest U.S. seashore cities, has been minimal for 100 years, a scientific fact that holds true for virtually all U.S. cities adjacent to oceans.[100] Is there any exception? I asked the IPCC in 2021 for an example of their claims of the acceleration of sea level rise and received no comment except that they would have some examples in the future.[101]

Baltimore: The sea level rise in Baltimore has been about average (about 3 mm/year) for both the U.S. and the world and has been consistent for over 110 years.

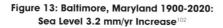

Figure 13: Baltimore, Maryland 1900-2020:
Sea Level 3.2 mm/yr Increase[102]

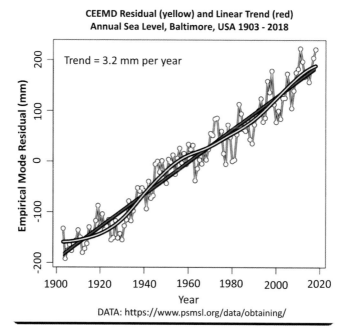

CEEMD Residual (yellow) and Linear Trend (red)
Annual Sea Level, Baltimore, USA 1903 - 2018

DATA: https://www.psmsl.org/data/obtaining/

Honolulu: A Hawaiian government study concluded that $15 billion will be required to address a sea level rise of 3 feet (915 mm) by 2100.[103] This remarkable prediction is four times the current rate of sea level rise, which has been constant at 3 mm per year for decades. The chart below confirms that Honolulu has seen no acceleration in sea levels during the past 100 years despite continuous increases in CO_2.

Figure 14: Honolulu, Hawaii:
Sea Level Rise 3.1 mm/year (1/8 inch)

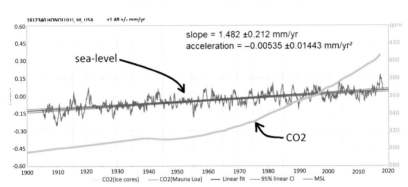

Figure 15: Beach Sizes Remain about the Same during the Past
100 Years at Waikiki Beach

If sea levels were rising at anything like the rates predicted by the Hawaiian government and Activists, we would likely see its effects on the hotels that line the beaches of Honolulu. But if you are lucky enough to go there to research this issue, you will see that even historic hotels, such as the Moana Surfrider Hotel on Waikiki Beach, built in 1901, are still there, *right on the beach,* and doing just fine. This totally contradicts Activist claims of significant sea level rise. Later in this chapter, I will explain why the U.N. IPCC makes such erroneous and frightening sea level projections.

Hilo and Miami Beach: Hilo, Hawaii, on the Big Island, and Miami Beach, Florida, are both examples of how the land sinking due to compaction (subsidence) affects sea levels. In Hilo, the sea level has risen 3 mm/year for 100 years.[104]

Figure 16: Hilo, Hawaii: Sea Level Rise (3.12 mm/yr)[105]

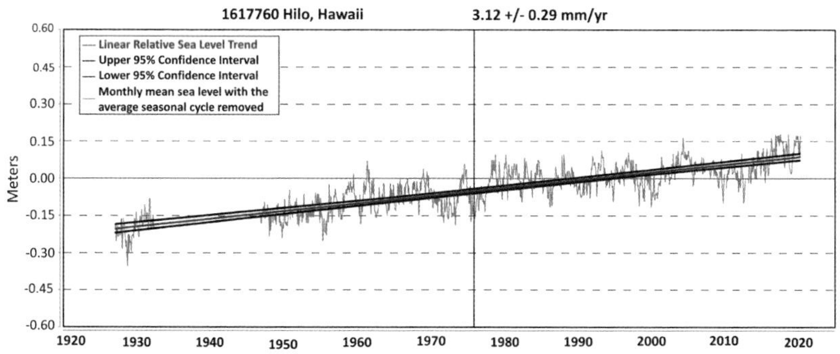

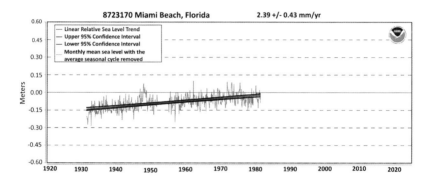

Figure 17: Miami Beach, Florida
Sea level increase from 1930-1980 was less than 4 inches[106]

In 1986, an EPA official predicted the sea level around Florida would rise 2 feet by 2020.[107] It never happened. According to SeaLevelRise.Org, an advocacy group that seems determined to scare people into taking action to stop what they claim is excessive global warming, the sea level in Miami "Is now rising by as much as 1 inch every 3 years."[108] But this is a multiple of reality and totally inconsistent with history because when NOAA measured sea levels at Miami Beach in the past, the water rose below the world average, rising only 2.4 mm (about 0.1 inches) per year.[109] In 1980, the U.S. Government stopped measuring the rise in Miami for some unknown reason. The closest location to Miami that I could find with U.S. government measurements was Gibara, Cuba (near Havana), which is 225 miles from Miami, where the sea level rise has been less than 6 inches in 100 years.[110]

Figure 18: Gibara, Cuba
The sea level rise is less than 6 inches in a century

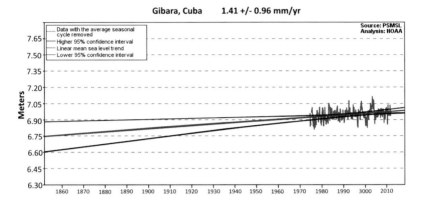

Gibara, Cuba   1.41 +/- 0.96 mm/yr

Many believe that recent flooding in Miami is a direct result of global warming. However, this is disputed by a joint sea rise study by universities in Miami, Florida and Padua, Italy,[111] which concluded that the major cause of flooding was subsidence. The study determined that the ground was sinking due to mud and peat fill material compacting by about 1 inch in 10 years.[112] Climate change is not to blame.

Lake Michigan: Many U.S. government predictions of changes in the levels of inland waters have also been faulty. In 2012, when the water levels in the Great Lakes were historically low, NOAA blamed global warming and warned that we should expect even lower levels in the future.[113] But then the water levels started to rise in 2013, and by 2017 NOAA claimed that this increase was also due to global warming.[114] By 2019, this claim proved to be questionable.[115] [116] But Climate Activists are clever and have now adopted the Thermos Bottle Defense and now tell us that climate change causes the *volatility* of Lake Michigan's height.[117] [118] (A thermos bottle keeps hot things hot and cold things cold. How does it do that?) History has proven that the quantities of rain and snow are more accurate predictors of Lake Michigan's height than the computer projections of the Activists.

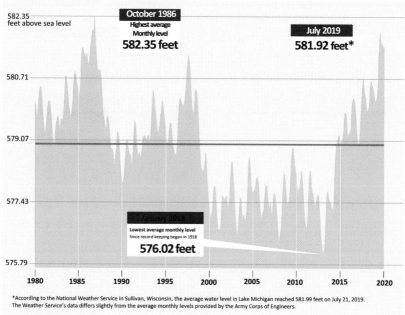

Figure 19: Lake Michigan: 1980-2020 Water Height

Lake Michigan-Huron monthly water levels 1980-2020   **Mean long-term average level**

Since the mid-1980s, monthly water levels for Lake Michigan-Huron have hit record highs and lows.

*According to the National Weather Service in Sullivan, Wisconsin, the average water level in Lake Michigan reached 581.99 feet on July 21, 2019. The Weather Service's data differs slightly from the average monthly levels provided by the Army Corps of Engineers.

Source: Army Corps of Engineers

Why Some Projections of Sea Level Rise Are So Poor

Let me address the question of why the Activist projections of sea level rise have been so consistently high. Earlier in this chapter, you read that Gore projected a 20-foot rise in the "near future;" that the U.N. projected "entire nations" will disappear under water; that there will be 50 million (or 2 billion) sea level refugees; and that sea levels will rise four times their current rates by 2100, due to global warming. All these predictions have either not happened or there has been almost no indication in nature that they will happen.

Despite these consistent failures to match reality, the Activists have recently doubled down. In addition to the false claims above, we are now told in the *New York Times*, "a report lays out climate's threat to U.S. security,"[119]

and the Department of Homeland Security (DHS) has issued a report that
"tens of millions" (as many as 143 million) will likely be climate-change-
displaced by 2050.[120]

The Activists and Their Imaginary Calculations of Sea Level Rise

When one examines *how* the Activists do their calculations of sea level rise,
it becomes obvious *why* their accuracy is so poor: The Activist U.N. IPCC
predictions do not focus on actual measurements of sea level rise. Instead,
they concentrate on mathematical regression analysis using factors, including their estimates of historical changes in the size of glaciers. I believe
the imagination they show relating to sea levels is one of the highlights of
their 3,000-page 2021 climate change report.[121] As you would expect, the
Activists predict disaster and categorize our situation as **CODE RED**.[122]

The Activist mathematical regression analysis to determine sea level rise
since 1900 includes the following factors to determine global sea level rise:

- Change in Antarctic glaciers, Greenland glaciers, and other glaciers
- Temperature changes
- Barometric changes

Here are their conclusions:

- In 1900, seas rose 1.3 mm/year
- By 1971 seas rose 1.9 mm/year
- By 2006 seas rose 3.7 mm/year

The following chart approximates the difference between the U.N.
measurements and the Earth's empirical history of actual sea level rise.

**Figure 20: U.N. Activist's Calculation and Prediction
of Sea Level Rise vs Actual Historic Rise**[123]

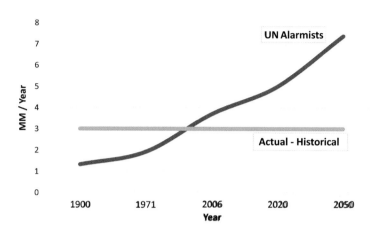

The fundamental Activist error of measuring sea level change by a bunch of parameters rather than measuring the sea-level changes directly was identified by Plato 2500 years ago. In his book, *The Republic,*[124] commonly read in Philosophy 101, Plato wrote *The Allegory of the Cave,*[125] where the following situation is described: A group of people has never seen the light of day because they have lived in a cave since birth. They can only look straight ahead and in no other direction because they are totally bound. Behind them is a fire, and behind the fire is a partial wall. Outside the wall, there are people who move statues of men and women. The prisoners can only see shadows of the moving statues which are reflected on the wall by the fire. Because the prisoners are bound and can only see the shadows, they believe the shadows are real men and women. Thus, they confuse the shadows for reality.

When the Activist scientists at the U.N. IPCC measure sea level rise, they estimate changes in the glaciers and other factors, which are only the shadows of real sea level rising. We know they are wrong because when sea levels are directly measured, they differ significantly from the Activist estimates. This explains why Activist U.N. scientists claim that the average sea level rise has accelerated from 1.3 mm to 3.9 mm per year during the past 120 years is so inaccurate. They are not matching nature; they seem to believe they are improving upon nature. Their forecasts of large near term rises in the sea level produce fear where there is no reason to fear.

When I contacted one of their "experts," a thought leader in the U.N. IPCC group, I requested the following, "Please send to me your list of locations and cities for which there has been an acceleration in sea levels consistent with the U.N. IPCC conclusions." I wrote this request because I could not find even one location with accelerated sea levels."[126] As expected, there has been no answer. To my knowledge, *the Activist scientist experts at the U.N. IPCC have never identified one spot on Earth where sea levels have increased since 1900 from 1.3 mm to 3.9 mm.*

The Cost of Fear

Unfortunately, there is a cost of fear: The Activists tell us we must spend $400 Billion to protect our U.S. cities[127] , including New York City - $10 billion;[128] Florida - $76 billion[129]; and Houston - $26 billion.[130] However, we know that the sea levels in Houston have not risen more than 1 inch every 8 years. How much do you think we should spend on a problem that does not exist? What justification is there for fear?

Antarctica, the Arctic, and Greenland

There is much discussion and some disagreement as to what is happening to the world's glaciers. However, we do know that whether the total volume of glacial ice is rising or falling, sea levels have risen at a constant rate for over 100 years

Many major media articles on this subject claim that the melting of glacial ice will cause worldwide flooding.[131] NASA predicts: "If all glaciers and ice sheets melted, global sea level would rise by more than 195 feet."[132] Al Gore predicted incorrectly that there would be no snow on Mt. Kilimanjaro in 2020.[133] [134] In 2009, a U.S. Geological Survey ecologist incorrectly predicted the glaciers in Montana's Glacier National Park would disappear by 2020.[135] None of this has happened.

During the past several years, you have probably never seen an article in the media reporting that global warming is not causing glaciers to melt. Therefore you probably don't know that in November 2021, an early ice freeze in the Arctic just off Russia stranded 18 ships. In fact, according to Barents Sea Observer, ice almost 30 cm thick had spread across most of the East Siberian and Laptev seas.[136] It is unfortunate that the media ignores so much news that relates to unusually cold weather.

According to a University of Illinois study, there was no decrease in Global Sea Ice between 1980 and 2015.

Figure 21: No Decrease in Global Sea Ice for 35 Years

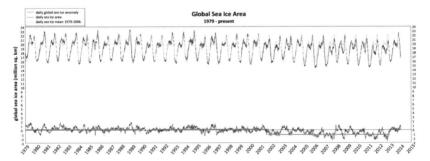

Antarctica: Antarctica has 90% of the world's iced landmass. The IPCC claims *with high confidence* that Antarctica has been losing mass. But this claim is highly contested by many sources, including the U.S. government (NASA). NASA tells us that the Antarctica ice sheet has been mostly growing for 10,000 years; [137] that the Antarctic ice, apart from a part of Western Antarctica, was growing annually by 100 gigatons (100,000,000,000 tons);[138] [139] [140] and that between 1979-2014 total Antarctic Sea ice increased by about 1% per decade before it recently started to fluctuate between decreasing and increasing. [141] [142]

From what I have studied, there seem to be conflicting measurements and limited convincing estimates of Antarctica's mass ice balance. We do know that there has been a cooling of about .5°C since 1998 in the Antarctic Peninsula.[143] Although there are benefits when ice melts, such as for communities that use glacial ice melt for drinking water, very few studies evaluate both the positive and negative aspects of ice melting. We are told by NASA that for the last 30 years, sea levels have risen a steady 1 inch every 8 years and we know that whether the ice is increasing or decreasing, the change has not affected humanity. Finally, *if you believe that we have serious issues relating to global ice melting, then ask yourself, where is all that melting ice going?*

Since Antarctica has 90% of Earth's total ice mass, shouldn't we be far less concerned about what is happening with the Arctic and Greenland, the cold spots at the opposite ends of the world?

The Arctic: Eric Post of UC Davis reported that the Arctic is warming faster than anywhere else on Earth, about 1°C during the past decade, and on track to be 4°C warmer by 2050. But many scientists, including Lord Monckton, believe that the Arctic ice cap recently has grown more in the winter than it shrinks in the summer,[144] and that even if the entire North Polar ice cap melted, since most of the North Polar ice cap is floating on water, melting would produce a sea level increase of only 1 mm and a temperature rise of .06°C.[145] Should we be worried?

Greenland: Al Gore told us that if the ice at Greenland disappeared, sea levels would rise between 18 and 20 feet.[146] But, the historical melting of Greenland's ice has not been significant and has been estimated to cause a rise of about .01 inches per year.[147 148 149 150 151] Nature magazine reported that Greenland lost about 3,900 billion tons of ice between 1992 and 2018, causing the mean sea level to rise by about 11 mm (about 1/2 of an inch).[152]

Conclusion

The scariest prediction made by Climate Activists is that sea level rise will accelerate and inundate coastal cities all around the world. If true, this would indeed be a catastrophe. But Activists base their predictions on inaccurate assumptions, faulty data, and unreliable computer models. Their predictions have failed repeatedly and are just plain unreliable.

Real-world data show that sea levels around the world have been rising slowly and at rates unchanged for hundreds of years. Any sea level rise due to melting ice at the poles is so small that it is almost invisible. The history of our climate is amazingly stable, and any climate disaster is many centuries away. There is simply no justification for the warnings, threats, fear, and guilt that Climate Activists attack us with daily.

Chapter 2 Quiz

	True	False
1. The acceleration in the rise in sea levels due to global warming and climate change has, as predicted by the U.N., caused over 50 million people to move from their homes.		
2. Sea levels are rising at significantly higher rates than they were 100 years ago.		
3. The melting of the polar ice caps has resulted in huge and accelerating sea level rises.		
4. The world's largest sea coast cities have seen huge increases in sea levels.		
5. The EPA and NOAA predictions in 2008 that Lake Michigan would continue to rise have proven true.		
6. Sea-level rise is ruining Hawaii's tourism business and causing shoreline hotels to topple into the ocean.		
7. The Arctic ice cap is melting at an alarming rate and will soon result in huge and accelerating sea- level rises.		
8. The Antarctic ice cap is also melting at an alarming rate, and it, too, will cause global sea levels to rise.		
9. Melting sea ice is contributing to rising sea levels.		

The answers to all of the questions are False. Here's why:

1. Sea Levels: Despite the U.N.'s claims that over 50 million people would be forced to move by 2010, there have been no sea level refugees.

2. According to the U.S. Geological Survey, sea levels began to rise 15,000 ago, and sea-level rises for the past 100 years have been small (about 3 mm per year) and not accelerating.

3. Polar Ice Caps: There have been small changes in the North and South Polar Caps. In total, sea levels have risen consistently about 3 millimeters (mm) per year for the last 100 years, and the melting polar caps are estimated to contribute about 1 mm per year.

4. All of the world's largest seacoast cities have seen constant small increases in sea levels (about 3 mm/ year). There has been no correlation between CO_2 growth and sea levels rising.

5. When the EPA and the NOAA, using computer predictions, concluded that because of global warming Lake Michigan water levels would rise, it sank. When they predicted that because of global warming Lake Michigan water levels would sink, it rose. Rain and snow levels have been far more accurate predictors of Lake Michigan's water levels.

6. Even Honolulu's famous Moana Surfrider Hotel on Waikiki Beach, built in 1901, is still at the shore and above water and doing well.

7. The Arctic ice cap may be losing some ice mass, but only at a slow and inconsistent rate.

8. The Antarctic ice cap is slowly gaining mass over time, offsetting much of the loss of ice from the Arctic ice cap. Only one small area of Antarctica is losing ice.

9. The global extent of sea ice varies but does not appear to be falling below historic levels. Since sea ice displaces water, it does not contribute to sea level rise when it melts.

FAKE NEWS: CODE RED! 1445 B.C. Pharaoh Amenhotep II declared that global warming and climate change caused the Red Sea to part. This was confirmed by the leading Swedish Climate Expert, an ancestor to Greta Thunberg, who explained that this was due to an Irreversible Chain Reaction and human induced global warming. This Expert called for a demonstration outside the pyramids for 1 million children who missed school and promised to never forgive those people who were responsible for generating so much carbon dioxide and exceeding the Climate Budget.

Summary

We should not fear, worry, or feel guilty about Global Warming or Climate Change because:

- There is virtually NO evidence that sea levels are rising faster now than 100 years ago.
- There are NO changes in the Polar Ice Caps that could lead to universal flooding.
- There is no reason to believe there will be millions of sea level refugees due to global warming and climate change.
- The Activist computer models always exaggerate future sea level rise, contradict reality, and ignore nature.

Chapter 3

Hurricanes, Forest Fires, and Droughts

"In order to counter misinformation, we need to understand the impact it has. The most obvious is causing us to believe things that aren't true."
(John Cook)

The author provides scientific information, primarily from the U.S. government, that there has been no increase in hurricanes, tornadoes, or flooding and that the weather on Earth has been amazingly stable for 100 years; that human activities, not climate change, are directly responsible for most forest fires; that psychiatrists are contributing to the alleged increase in climate-related mental illnesses; and how and why the Activists continually generate FAKE NEWS by confusing weather and climate.

Hurricanes and Cyclones

Before seriously examining the claimed problems with hurricanes, let me suggest that we recognize that they also have benefits: Milton Berle, a popular comedian in the 1950s, gave us an excellent example when he told us, "Florida hurricanes aren't all bad. The other day, my car got 200 miles to the gallon."

But back to reality.

Violent storms have different names depending on where they originate: Violent storms are called hurricanes when they form over the Atlantic and Northeast Pacific Oceans, typhoons when in the Northwest Pacific, and cyclones when over the Indian and South Pacific Oceans. Thanks to a constant barrage of scary headlines and selective reporting, the majority of Americans falsely believe that global warming is directly linked to a large increase in the number of these storms.[153]

U.S. government (NOAA)[154] studies confirm that there has been no increase in hurricanes: "It is premature to conclude that human activities and particularly greenhouse gas emissions have had a detectable impact on Atlantic hurricane or global tropical cyclone activity."[155] The U.N.'s IPCC agrees: "No robust trends in annual numbers of tropical storms, hurricanes, and major hurricane counts have been identified over the past 100 years in the North Atlantic basin."[156][157] Despite empirical evidence to the contrary, many groups, such as the World Wildlife Fund (WWF), warn us that future global warming will create more hurricanes.[158]

However, the Activists, searching for proof of climate change, have switched to a "change of location" argument: that there are more hurricanes in the North Atlantic and Central Pacific and less in the Western Pacific and Southern Indian Ocean."[159] In other words, if you can't prove that hurricanes have increased, just claim that they have moved.

When we look at recent history, we find that there was a record low in major hurricanes during the 11 years prior to 2018, when only two hurricanes greater than Category 3 hit the continental United States.[160][161] The frequency of hurricanes on land in the U.S. has not increased during the past 50 years.[162 163]

Figure 22: 1880-2015 – No Increase in U.S. Hurricanes [164]
The U.S. Has Had No Increase in Major Land Hurricanes for 135 Years [165 166]

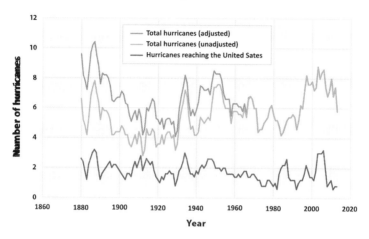

Figure 23: No Increase in Global Hurricanes or Tropical Storms [167]

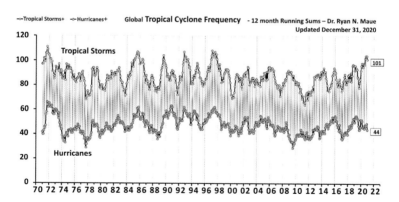

Having accepted the reality that there have been no more hurricanes, the Activists, in their efforts to generate fear and concern about global warming, now claim that we have a hurricane *intensity* problem. "Global warming is making hurricanes worse" reports the *Washington Post*.[168] How much worse? According to Elsner and Klang, during the past 30 years,

Category 4 and 5 hurricane speeds have increased 2%, which is about 3 miles out of 150 miles/hour.[169] [170] An increase of 2% is a minor variation and well within the margin of error. It could easily be biased by the selection process, timing, or other factors. This small claimed variation in intensity does not appear to be something to worry about. My request is that the next time you read an article claiming increased intensity of hurricanes, notice that it does *not* tell the reader how much more intense hurricanes are today compared to the past. The authors of articles that mention hurricane intensity either do not know or do not want you to know how low the claimed increase in intensity is.

The failure of the Activists to make their case regarding hurricanes is augmented by their failure to prove any connection between the rise in atmospheric carbon dioxide (CO_2) concentrations and the number of global hurricanes. The two are simply uncorrelated. See Figure 24.

Figure 24: More CO_2 but No More Hurricanes 2015-2020 [171] [172]

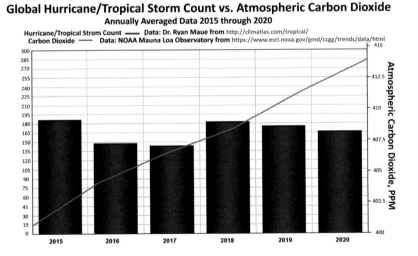

New York: It is very easy to find biased and selective facts in articles about the climate in most of the media. For example, a January 2022 article on hurricanes in Yahoo News reported that "Climate change will bring more hurricanes to New York," [173] where the study's author Joshua

Studholme, a Yale physicist, predicted that "hurricanes will appear in a wider range of latitudes than they have for the last 3 million years"[174] and that would represent "an important, under-estimated risk for climate change."[175] The article does not explain how many more hurricanes we should expect or whether all of them would be 2% more intense than the hurricanes of the past. It doesn't explain what we should do about more hurricanes (except perhaps worry).

Actually, New York has a rich history of hurricane activity since the 17th century, with the strongest hurricane hitting Long Island in 1938. In 2020 alone, there were nine hurricanes that impacted New York.[176] So why is Joshua Studholme telling us to worry about New York hurricanes in the future?

Tornadoes

Tornadoes are formed when the cool, dry air over the Rocky Mountains meets the warm, moist air in the Gulf of Mexico, causing violent swirling wind columns.[177] [178] The number of tornadoes has dropped from about 40 to about 30 per year. The year 2018 had the lowest tornado count in 60 years.[179] Meanwhile, deaths caused by tornadoes have dropped by 90% during the past 100 years.[180]

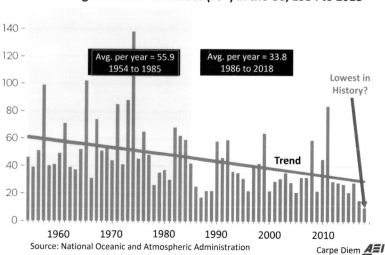

Figure 25: U.S. Tornadoes Drop 1954-2018 (NOAA) [181]

Strong to Violent Tornadoes (F3+) in the US, 1954 to 2018

Source: National Oceanic and Atmospheric Administration

Carpe Diem *AEI*

Forest Fires

Although the Activists claim that CO_2 is a major cause of forest fires, everyone accepts the fact that CO_2 is an excellent fire extinguisher. CO_2, in very high concentrations, is effective because it takes away oxygen, is very cold, and removes the heat from the fire.

Number of Fires

Historically, there is little basis for blame relating to the cause of more U.S. forest fires because there are now no more forest fires than in the past (U.S. Forest Service and National Interagency Fire Center). [182]

Figure 26: No Increase in U.S. Forest Fires 1983-2020 [183]

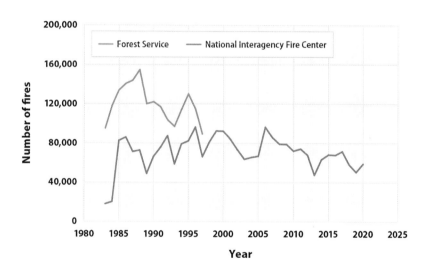

The **blue line** shows the total number of forest fires per year from 1983 to 2020. These totals include all reported forest fires, which can be as small as just a few acres.

Acreage Burned

If global warming were causing more forest fires in the U.S., we should be recording more acres of forests destroyed by fire over time. But real-world data shows just the opposite. During the past 20 years, the maximum yearly destruction by forest fires in the U.S. has been about 10 million acres, but before 1800, an average of over 100 million acres burned almost every year. This was 10 times the current forest acreage burn. In the Western U.S., it is estimated that in the 19th century, over 15 million acres burned each year. Actually, the acreage of forest fires has decreased significantly, and there has been no correlation between forest fires and temperature increase.

Figure 27: Reduction in Global Acreage Burned 1900-2010.[184]

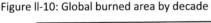

Figure II-10: Global burned area by decade

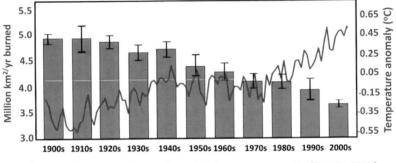

(Source data: Burned area: Yang 2014; temperature: HadCRUT4 2017)

The orange bars show a steady decrease in acreage burned globally. The red line shows the increase in average world temperatures.

The Major Cause of Forest Fires: Arson and other Human Activities

The Economist tells us that in 2020 California was hotter and drier than previously, and this was directly the result of global warming.[185] The 2020 fires included *The August Complex Fire,* a combination of about 40 different fires, which burned over 1 million acres.

The Economist does not mention that multiple fires were set by arsonists in California in 2020. The largest arson-caused fire engulfed more than 100,000 acres in Monterey, California alone.[186] [187]

Dr. Jon Keeley, a U.S. Geological Survey scientist, stated, "most of these fires are almost all started by people. California doesn't get any lightning during these Santa Ana winds. However, the more people that inhabit the area, the higher the probability that somebody will start a fire. … (California) is very densely populated, making people more likely to start a fire during these episodes."[188]

That the basic cause of forest fires is human action is supported by the U.S. Government's Department of the Interior, which blamed humans for up to 90% of all U.S. forest fires,[189] and Jennifer Balch, Director of the Earth Lab Project and University of Colorado professor, concluded that 84% of all U.S. fires are human caused,[190][191] primarily from utilities, vehicles, smoking, arson, human error, and motorized equipment.[192][193]

The U.S. Forest Service reported that during the 20th century, over 2,000 forest fires out of about 2,500 were started by humans.[194] Because humans cause such a high percentage of forest fires and the acreage burned, how can anyone reasonably claim that climate change has anything to do with increasing forest fires? Logically, to continue to reduce forest fires, we should concentrate on the human factor.

Since 1944, the U.S. Forest Service has recognized that people, not climate, are the major cause of forest fires and reminds us through Smokey the Bear: "Only You Can Prevent Forest Fires."

There are also fire reduction policies that make sense. Thinning forests, especially those adjacent to homes and human development, seems quite reasonable.[195]

John Donne,[196] an English clergyman and poet who lived 400 years ago, probably knew little about forest fires, but he accurately described how arson and other human activities were the primary cause when he wrote, "Do not ask for whom the Bell tolls; it tolls for thee!"[197]

Heat Waves

We are told in the media and by the United Nations that Death Valley hit an all-time high temperature of 130°F on August 18, 2020, and that this is proof that global warming is "real."[198 199] Somehow, the authors of these reports manage to ignore the fact that on July 10, 1913, the temperature in Death Valley was 134°F.[200] A typical pronouncement from the World Meteorological Organization (WMO) reads: "Heat waves were the deadliest meteorological hazards in the 2015-2019 period affecting all continents and resulting in numerous new temperature records."[201] But the WMO defines heat waves as 5 degrees above average temperatures for five days. For example, since 5 degrees above average for Nome, Alaska in January is still freezing,[202] even very cold periods are classified by the WMO as heat waves.

If we use a different definition of a heat wave, say a series of days when the temperature exceeds 100°F, the results are quite different. According to the U.S. Environmental Protection Agency (EPA), during the past 80 years, days when the temperature exceeded 100°F in the United States decreased from 1.5% of all days to about 1%.[203] More weather stations registered 100°F or more during the 1930s than during any of the past 15 years.[204] There are no more U.S. heat waves now than there were in 1900,[205] when atmospheric CO_2 levels were much lower.

Figure 28: U.S. 100 F (1895-2015) [206]

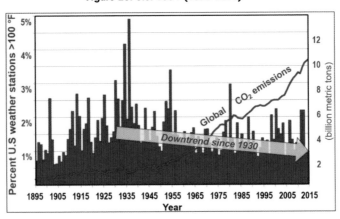

In Figure 28, the **blue line** shows global CO_2 emissions while the **red columns** show the percentage of U.S. weather stations reporting temperatures greater than 100°F each year between 1895 and 2015. The **red columns** show a *downward trend* in the percentage of weather stations reporting 100°F days, while the **blue line** shows an *upward trend* in global CO_2 emissions. There is no correlation between the two.

Droughts

For the past 50 years, NASA and many climate experts have incorrectly predicted more droughts due to climate change.[207] The prediction that droughts would cause America to ration water by 1974[208] proved false, as did predictions of significant U.S. droughts in the Southeast and Midwest.[209] Despite consistent erroneous predictions that droughts would trigger human tragedy, Activists continue with massive, continuous media support of their frightening predictions.[210] [211] In the U.S., major droughts occurred between 1700 and 1820. About 75% of the most severe droughts since 1900 occurred during the first half of the 20th century.[212] Meanwhile, over 300,000 square kilometers of arid soil have become greener during the past 30 years.[213]

Figure 29: No Increase in Droughts during the Past 135 Years[214]

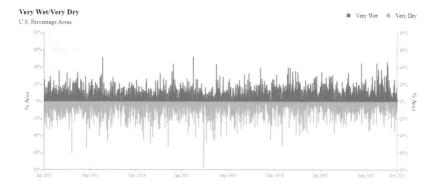

Floods

"Coastal flooding will create an exodus of eco-refugees, threatening political chaos," according to a 1989 U.N. pronouncement.[215] Since warmer air can contain more moisture, the argument goes, there should be more precipitation in a warmer world and, therefore, more flooding, or to use the scientific term, "extreme streamflow." However, the most extensive study on streamflow, conducted by Gregory McCabe and David Wolock and published in 2014, examined the streamflow for more than 500 rivers between 1950 and 2010 and concluded there was minimal impact by human activity.[216]

The largest American flood of the 19th century was the Great Mississippi flood of 1851. It resulted from record-setting rainfalls when temperatures were cooler than they are now, and CO_2 levels were 25% lower than today. Another significant flood was the Great Mississippi River Flood of 1844, the largest flood ever recorded on the Missouri River and Upper Mississippi River in terms of discharge. The Great Flood of 1862 was the "worst disaster ever to strike California."[217] All of these events took place more than 150 years ago, long before CO_2 emissions could have played any role.

The major flood during the 20th century was the Great Mississippi Flood of 1927, which covered 27,000 square miles and produced water depths of up to 30 feet for several months. The cost of the damage in 1927 dollars was at least $250 million (this would be several billion dollars in current dollar value).[218]

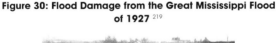

Figure 30: Flood Damage from the Great Mississippi Flood of 1927 [219]

In China in 2020, a major flood displaced more than 700,000 people, affected more than 60 million, and caused more than $150 billion in damage.[220] Global warming at work? Probably not. The Chinese have records of floods going back some 4,000 years, including reports of floods that were surely as large or larger, though of course they affected fewer people because the country's population was smaller at the time. The Great Flood of 1900 BC stands out as one of enormous magnitude.[221] It is possible that the ancestors of China's Climate Activists were on the scene some 4,000 years ago because, according to Chinese tradition, the Great Flood occurred as a "universal punishment for human sin."[222]

In 2020, there were major floods in many places throughout the world, including Indonesia, Japan, and Nepal. But once again, these locations have flooded for centuries. For example, Jakarta, Indonesia, has had a dozen major floods since 1621.[223]

When one considers the facts delineated above, it is hard to conclude that the Earth has a larger flooding issue than in the past. However, we can be certain that every time there is a flood, the Activists will inform us that this is yet another global warming disaster.

Major Climatic Events and Mental Health

Even though there have been no more hurricanes, tornadoes, forest fires, droughts, or floods than usual, many mental health experts tell us that diseases from climate change and global warming have never been worse. We are told that climate change is causing "more mental illness," including the "disorder of event exposure."[224] How concerned and worried should we be about "disorders of event exposure?" Do you think "event exposure" is covered by Medicare?

An American Psychiatric Association (APA) article, *How Extreme Weather Events Affect Mental Health*,[225] is an excellent example of fear-mongering where there is nothing to fear. The article tells us that climate change causes anxiety and chronic and severe mental health disorders. Do you believe that a 1°C increase in temperature in 140 years is really causing more mental disorders? The APA tells us that flooding can cause depression and post-traumatic stress disorder. But there is no more flooding than there was 100 years ago. Almost half of Americans believe climate change negatively affects mental health. Could one reason for this belief be that the APA tells us that climate change causes mental health problems?

In the article, the APA further tells us that climate change is already causing population migration and that last year, 20 million people were forced to move because of climate change.[226] Which 20 million people? Where did they go? If you can solve this mystery, please let me know.

Activists Confuse Weather and Climate

Sometimes I feel sorry for the Activists because they don't seem to know the difference between weather and climate. Here is what the Merriam Webster's dictionary tells us:

Weather: State of the atmosphere *at a particular time and place*. [227]

Climate: The usual weather conditions *over a period of years*. [228]

Merriam Webster tells us that one hurricane is a weather event. This is **not** evidence of climate change which requires several years. According to the dictionary, it would require at least several years to consider any type of weather (hurricanes, tornadoes, floods) a climate change.

English is a wonderful language in which words have specific meanings. As Professor Henry Higgins said in *My Fair Lady*, "The majesty and grandeur of the English Language, it is the greatest possession we have."[229] And English, when it is not corrupted by bias or ignorance, clearly enables us to distinguish and clarify our thinking. Why is it that so many climate articles include the thought that a singular event (a hurricane or a tornado) is a valid example of climate change? As the dictionary informs us, a singular event is a weather event; to verify climate change requires years. To cite another comment by Professor Higgins, "There even are places where English completely disappears: In America, they haven't used it for years."[230] Perhaps, his comment applies to the Activists when they mislead us by claiming that one weather event is proof of climate change.

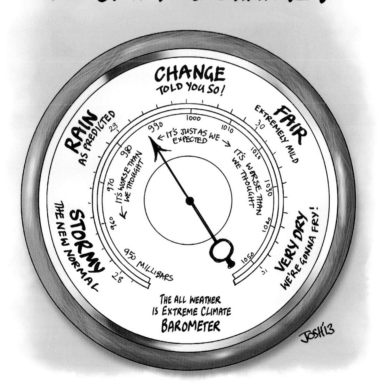

Real News versus Fake News

The efforts by Activists to confuse weather with climate have little to do with science and much to do with politics. Articles that would confirm the reality of fewer hurricanes, tornadoes, or forest fires would be **Real News**. The dictionary confirms that it is **Fake News** when the Activists confuse weather and climate and claim that a single storm is proof of climate change. Of course, there has been some climate change, but our climate has been amazingly stable for the past 100 years. There has been very little climate change, but politically the Activists want us to be concerned and worried.

Why is this Activist **Fake News** political? Because it pushes us to support governments' demands for additional power over people's lives. Any government entity that controls CO_2 can regulate where people live, how and if they travel, and even what they can eat. The Paris Accord, which will be discussed later, allows 200 national governments to control the production and use of fossil fuels. Since there has been no climate change attributable to mankind's use of fossil fuels, why should we allow governments to attack fossil fuel use? What exactly are the benefits?

In summary, this chapter has explained the shoddy science that falsely identified hurricanes, tornadoes, and forest fires as serious climate change problems and revealed how the Activist "facts" are contrary to actual empirical climate data from the last 100 years.

Chapter 3 Quiz

	True	False
1. The United Nations' Intergovernmental Panel on Climate Change (IPCC) found global warming is causing an increase in the number and intensity of hurricanes.	☐	☐
2. The number and intensity of hurricanes making landfall in the United States as well as globally have been increasing in recent decades.	☐	☐
3. The number of tornadoes in the United States has risen over time as a result of global warming.	☐	☐
4. The number of deaths caused by tornadoes and the amount of damage to property has increased during the past 100 years.	☐	☐
5. The number and intensity of forest fires in the United States have increased during the past 100 years.	☐	☐
6. Heat waves became more common and more deadly in the United States as the climate steadily warmed during the twentieth century.	☐	☐
7. The percentage of the U.S. landmass experiencing drought grew during the twentieth century.	☐	☐
8. Recent floods in the United States have been the largest in the historical record, proving they are the result of global warming and not just natural variability.	☐	☐
9. Countries around the world are experiencing record-setting floods.	☐	☐
10. The United Nations' prediction made in 1989 that coastal flooding would create millions of "eco-refugees" has proven to be correct.	☐	☐

The answers to all of the questions are False. Here's why:

1. The IPCC found there was insufficient evidence to conclude that global warming is causing an increase in the number or intensity of hurricanes.

2. Records clearly show the number and intensity of hurricanes making landfall in the United States as well as globally have been falling, not rising, in recent decades.

3. The number of tornadoes in the United States has also been falling over time, even as atmospheric carbon dioxide levels have risen over time.

4. The number of deaths caused by tornadoes has fallen by an astounding 90 percent during the past century.

5. Both the number of forest fires and the number of acres burned have fallen during the past century. The major cause of forest fires is not the weather but human activities, including arson and power lines.

6. The percentage of weather stations in the United States recording temperatures above 100°F fell during the twentieth century.

7. Drought actually became less widespread in the United States during the twentieth century. About 75 percent of the most severe droughts occurred during the first half of the past 120 years.

8. The biggest floods in the history of the United States occurred before human carbon dioxide emissions could have played a role.

9. None of the floods that occurred recently in other countries are outside the range of natural variability. China, which has records reaching back thousands of years, recorded many floods worse than those it is experiencing today.

10. There has been no massive increase in the number of people forced to move due to flooding or any of the other alleged consequences of global warming.

FAKE NEWS: CODE RED! In 2042, the U.S. government departments (NASA, NOAA, and the EPA) responsible for verifying global warming and climate change once again failed in their mission to terrorize the population with fear. Once again, as was the case in 2021, there were no significant climate changes (long-term weather trends): Hurricane and tornado activity continued to stay constant, as well as forest fires, droughts, floods, and heat waves. The world continued to show warmer winters, cooler summers, warmer nights, and cooler days. If anything, the weather continued to improve.

The Activists from 300 governments met in Gilega (previously known as Kitega), Burundi, a country so poor that the Activists complained the hotel with the pool had no swim-up bar. One basic problem they faced was that the Universal Climate Fear Index (the percentage of people who were scared stiff by global warming and climate change) had dropped below 50%, and support for spending trillions of dollars to prevent climate change was disappearing.

The major decision of the Burundi Agreement was that the U.N. IPCC scientists would receive funding to buy $10 billion in new supercomputers. The U.N. scientists guaranteed that these monies, combined with their creativity and imagination, would provide predictions of significant future global warming and climate change. For example, they had high confidence that they could prove that future heat waves in Nome, Alaska, could raise temperatures in January to at least 10 degrees below zero; that the world's hurricane center would move to Topeka, Kansas; and that the Amargosa River would flood Death Valley, California. The Activists have already had one major victory as the citizens of Uruguay immediately decided to give up eating meat.

––––––––––

Summary:

We should not fear, worry, or feel guilty about global warming or climate change because:

- There are NO more hurricanes, tornadoes, fires, droughts, or floods than in the past.
- For the past 100 years, there has been no change in major climatic events while the CO_2 in the atmosphere has continually increased.

Chapter 4
Extinctions

"Scientific confidence is strongest when many different lines of evidence all point to a single conclusion."
(John Cook)

The author explains that only the outstanding creativity, imagination, and bias of the Climate Activists could possibly put forth the preposterous conclusion that climate change has or is likely to cause the extinction of polar bears or the disappearance of the coral reefs; that the Climate Activists should feel guilty for promoting this misinformation; and that the real threats to these animals come from hunting, fishing, and the expansion of human agricultural and commercial endeavors.

This chapter discusses the extinction of animals. According to a 2019 report by the U.N. IPCC, the world's largest Climate Activist organization, one-third of all species could be extinct by 2070,[231] and one million species of plants and animals are at risk of extinction with an extremely strong connection between "biodiversity loss and climate change."[232] [233] [234] These frightening predictions have been promoted by the media for 50 years, ever since Paul Ehrlich told us that by 1985, "All important animal life in the sea will be extinct."[235] [236]

Thankfully, reality is very different. As shown below, the small amount of global warming has virtually no effect on the number of extinctions of animals on Earth. Activists deploy their weapons of misinformation, scare tactics, and selective facts. They attempt to censor and intimidate the Climate Realists who disagree with them when the Realists dare to point out historical and empirical data that contradict Activist predictions.

Polar Bears

In discussing the extinction of animals, it is appropriate to start with the polar bear because this animal is the poster child for the Activists' false claims of massive animal extinction due to global warming. Quite likely,

the first website about polar bears that will come up in a Google search will be the World Wildlife Foundation (WWF) which tells you that you can "Help save the polar bear" by fighting climate change.[237] The WWF will inform you that polar bears are necessary because they "are at the top of the food chain and have an important role in the overall health of the marine environment."[238]

Al Gore would agree. He warned us in *An Inconvenient Truth* (2006) that the serious loss of ice, starting in the 1970s at the North Pole, was "bad news for the polar bears," which travel from ice floe to ice floe hunting seals. Gore tells us that "A new scientific study shows that, for the first time, polar bears have been drowning in significant numbers. … these bears find they must swim much longer distances from floe to floe."[239]

Al Gore's concern about polar bears dying should be highly discounted because polar bears which live farther south, where there is *less ice,* weigh about 50 pounds *more* than those which live farther north, where there is more ice.[240] [241] It was true that the polar bear was headed toward extinction 50 years ago, but it had nothing to do with global warming. The fact is that for centuries too many polar bears were hunted and killed for their skins.[242] This is why they were headed toward extinction and a justification for the U.S. National Forest Service to order the prohibition of killing polar bears. The countries where almost all of the polar bears live have signed international agreements to protect them.[243]

The U.S. Fish and Wildlife Service (FWS), which enforced the 1973 Endangered Species Act, predicted that by 2008 the polar bear population would shrink by two-thirds. Actually, polar bear populations have increased despite many being killed by poachers as trophies and for their skins; and by the native Inuit, who by agreement with the Canadian government are allowed to kill 600 polar bears annually.[244 245 246 247]

Historically polar bears had proven to be a hearty species and thrived 20,000 years ago when temperatures were eight degrees warmer.[248 249] Not one or two degrees warmer, *eight degrees* warmer! The truth is that between 1970 and 2015, polar bear populations increased from about 10,000 to about 30,000.[250 251 252]

The good news is that because of these real facts, you can honestly tell your friends that there are very few exhausted or drowning polar bears. The current Activist claim of the impending extinction of polar bears is fiction.[253] Recently a conservative group posted on social media that the polar bears were doing just fine and were not headed toward extinction. As a result, the conservative group was removed from social media by the "Fact Checkers."[254]

Susan Crockford[255] studied polar bear populations and was terminated as a professor at the University of Victoria because her results contradicted claims of impending polar bear extinction.[256] Here are the results of Crockford's study of the polar bear population.[257]

Figure 31: Crockford's Study of Polar Bear Growth[258]

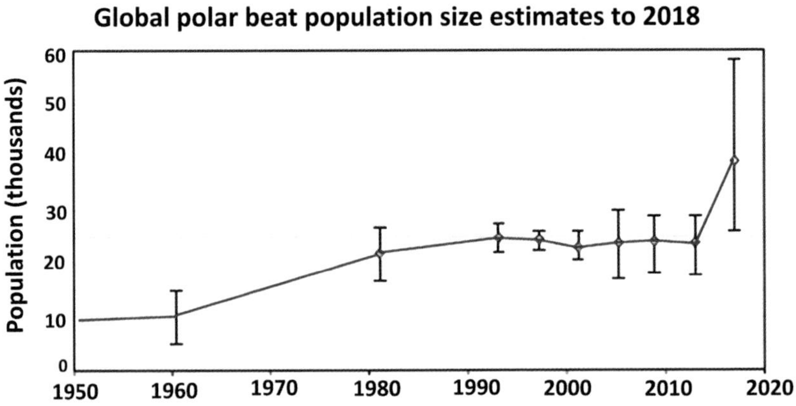

Global polar beat population size estimates to 2018

Coral Reefs

Coral reefs cover less than 1% of the ocean floor, but they are home to over a quarter of all marine life. They consist of thousands of tiny soft-bodied animals called polyps or corals, which excrete a hard outer skeleton of calcium carbonate (limestone) that attaches to either rock or the skeletons of previously living polyps.[259] [260] They are animals because, unlike plants, they do not make their own food. They have tiny arms that capture food from the water and put it in their mouths.[261]

With little effort, you will be able to find numerous articles about the imminent extinction of the coral reefs. For example, *The Independent* reports, "More than 90% of world's coral reefs will die by 2050." [262] The Activists claim that because there is more atmospheric CO_2, there will be higher CO_2 levels in the ocean which will destroy the coral reefs by reducing the water's pH level. You may recall that pH is a chemical scale that specifies how acidic (1-7 pH) or alkaline (7-14 pH) a body of water is. Pure water has a pH of 7. The oceans and seawaters fluctuate between 7.8 pH and 8.3 pH and average about 8 pH.

Any reduction in pH should be called "Reduced Alkalinity," but the Activists call it *"Ocean Acidification,"* which sounds ominous and identifies the change in pH as more of a cataclysmic event.[263] Studies by NOAA[264] and Wallace[265] in 2016 determined that there was a reduction of only about 0.1 in pH levels (from 8.15 pH to 8.05 pH) during the past 100 years, as shown on the next page.[266]

Figure 32: The Oceans: A Reduction of .1 pH in 100 Years

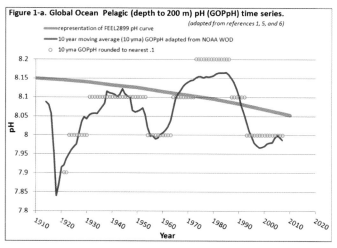

1915-2015 Global Ocean pH[267] [268]

The Activists claim that the coral reefs will disappear because the higher CO_2 will cause a lower pH that will weaken the coral exoskeletons.[269] [270] It is hard to totally blame CO_2 since the pH was lower in 1915 than now, and the corals survived (see the chart above).[271] [272] Besides, it is well-established that there are many causes of coral deaths, including: "Natural enemies,[273] coral mining, pollution (organic and non-organic), overfishing, blast fishing, the digging of canals and access into islands and bays."[274] To scientifically prove that it is the pH that is killing the coral, the Climate Activists must prove that the factors listed above are not significant influencers in the real world – rather than in test tubes.[275]

The sunscreen chemicals in suntan lotions, according to the National Ocean Service, "threaten corals and other marine life in serious ways. That includes accumulating in the tissue of coral, which can deform young coral and kill them." [276] [277] Multiple localities with coral reef bleaching have passed laws against suntan lotions with certain components. Key West, Florida, and Hawaii have banned sunscreens containing oxybenzone and octanoate.[278] [279] Worldwide, between 6,000 and 14,000 tons of sunscreen are deposited on coral reefs each year by vacationers.[280] Other examples of human-caused damage to coral reefs include agricultural runoff and copper from boat marine paints which have caused *multifocal purple spots disease* in the Puerto Rican coral.[281]

The country of Palau is a group of Pacific islands, warmer and closer to the equator than Australia. U.S government scientists proved that in the Palau coral reefs, where the pH is very low (7.8 pH), the diversity and strength of the corals were strongest. Their scientific study concluded that "the lower pH areas were found to host a greater number of coral species and to cover a greater portion of the seafloor" and that corals in low pH areas were outperforming those living in higher pH conditions further from the islands.[282] [283]

Why don't more people know this? One reason is that most people have never heard of Ed Warner! Warner went to Palau as a member of the *Micronesia Challenge* to document coral behavior in 2020.[284] He saw both beauty and strength in the coral reefs which existed in these unusually low pH waters and wrote an article, *How Palau protects its reefs and waters*.[285] [286]

Of course, to get approval for funding and publication, the following disclaimer was required: "The world's coral reefs are under threat, both from increased ocean temperatures and from acidification due to the burning of fossil fuels."[287] But the research cited in the article disputes that comment and demonstrates how reality contradicts the disclaimer.

Figure 33: Coral Reefs in Palau at maximum "Acidification" Thriving [288]

Here are Warner's observations: The Palau reefs were bleached in 1998 and had "turned to rubble." By 2012 the rubble had made a major recovery and now multiple corals were growing extremely well where the water was more acidic than anything predicted by the Activists. In 2020, Warner reported the causes of the pre-1998 bleaching: "Palau faced a crisis. Growing tourism was producing a rapid increase in trash in the waters and shoreline." Palau cleaned up the trash and declared the use of 10 different ingredients in sunscreen illegal. As a result, the coral thrived. If you happen to run into an Activist, feel free to ask him why the coral reefs thrive in the extremely warm 28°C temperatures and low pH in the waters around Palau.[289] [290] [291]

Unless you have been living in a cave, you most certainly have been told that the Great Barrier Reef (GBR) corals are bleaching and that this is a new phenomenon caused exclusively by climate change. But it is not a new phenomenon, as verified by a study by Nicholas Kamenos and Sebastian Hennige: "We found that widespread bleaching had been occurring there since at least the 1600s."[292] The problem with the Activist fact is that it is not true.

The 5 million GBR tourists each year[293] have a role in causing the GBR to weaken and lose color. Wendy Syfret reported that "Your Sunscreen is destroying the GBR, and human activities like *dumping dredge waste* has already knocked out half of the GBR."[294] Also, Selina Ward, a professor at the University of Queensland, has proven that sunscreen chemicals in high concentrations exist where tourists are most prevalent.[295]

Can you picture a university professor fired for stating that the primary cause of problems at the GBR is something other than global warming? Well, picture it now. Peter Ridd was fired from James Cook University for *conduct breaches* when he said that the research by the Centre of Excellence for Coral Reef Science, which claims that global warming is destroying the GBR, was false.[296] This is censorship through intimidation, pure and simple.

Figure 34: Map Showing the Location of the Kimberly Reefs
Australia's Kimberley Coral Reefs

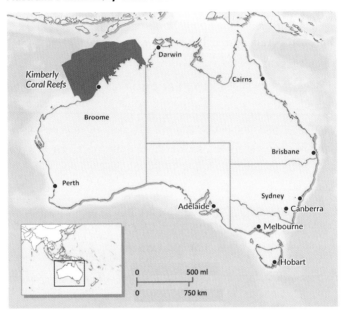

Source: Centre for Conservation Geography; Land and Bathymetry from Natural Earth
© 2019 The Pew Charitable Trusts

I have included one more example that contradicts the Climate Activists' claim that coral reefs will disappear. This is not because I am trying to bore you; it is because the extinction of the coral reefs is a major talking point of the Activists.

The Kimberley Coral Reefs are located 160 miles off Australia's northwest coast. According to The Pew Charitable Trusts, this "Thriving Australian reef shows what's possible when ecosystems are untouched by humans. The relatively pristine region has some of the world's most unusual and resilient coral reefs ... with some boasting greater diversity (400 species) than the famed corals of the Great Barrier Reef." A story about the study in the *Guardian* reported, "Corals here have adapted to thrive in extreme environmental conditions including high temperatures ... making them some of the most robust and resilient coral communities known to science." [297] [298]

The Kimberley Coral Reefs are significant because if global warming were causing harm to coral reefs, we would see it here in a region where other human influences are less present. The fact that they are thriving despite high temperatures and lower pH is an indication that global warming poses no threat to corals worldwide.

The Activists should also know that the U.S. government (NOAA) has identified natural threats to coral reefs, including waves from hurricanes; long periods of low tides that expose the reefs to ultraviolet radiation; El Niño that can cause increased salinity; and barnacles, crabs and sea stars which prey on the inner tissues of the coral polyps.[299]

Animal Non-Extinctions

Extinct Animals: One of the earliest claims by the Activists is that the Dodo bird, which lived on the island of Mauritius in the Indian Ocean, became extinct about 1682 due to climate change.[300] As the *Guardian* reported, the Dodo bird was "a resilient animal whose demise was caused by an ecological disaster."[301] Curiously, the internet includes the claim that the Dodo is just one of the "animals recently extinct."[302] The Dodo bird had no natural enemies until humans settled there in the 16th century and killed many for their tasty meat.[303] Humans brought in pigs and monkeys, natural enemies of the Dodo bird, which killed many of them.

It appears that the *Guardian* erred in its claim that climate change killed the Dodo bird and that, in this case, it failed to achieve its mission: "We're committing to another year of high-impact reporting that can counter misinformation and offer an authoritative, trustworthy source of news for everyone." [304]

If you search Google for extinct animals, you will likely find a site [305] [306] headlined *Animals That Have Gone Extinct due to Global Warming,*[307] which includes the polar bear, the Adélie Penguin, and the North Atlantic Cod.[308] We know that the polar bear is not extinct, and there are millions of Adélie Penguins and North Atlantic Cod. What happened to our Google Fact Checker?

Here are the six animals that were listed under the headline "Extinct Animal."

#1. The Golden Toad: The site claims that the Golden Toad of Costa Rica became extinct due in part to climate change.[309] But a team of experts from the University of Maryland, in an article titled Global *Warming Didn't Kill the Golden Toad* declared the innocence of global warming and that the Golden Toads died from a serious skin disease.[310] Other contributing factors included significant deforestation and forest clearing after 1940, and "by 1983 only the less accessible high-rainfall zones in rugged terrain … (were) relatively undisturbed." [311] [312] Global warming had nothing to do with the toad's demise.[313] [314]

Golden Toad

#2. Polar Bear: The headline cited above contradicts the fact that polar bears are not extinct.[315]

#3. Adélie Penguin: Not yet extinct! According to the World Wildlife Fund (WWF) the Adélie Penguin is "the most widespread species of penguin" and they are "increasing in Antarctica."[316]

#4. North Atlantic Cod: The claim is false! Currently, the North Atlantic Cod population is increasing[317] despite human consumption of over 2 million pounds yearly.[318] About 50 times a year, I have an Atlantic Cod sandwich at Culver's, a chain of about 800 restaurants, and if these Cod were to become extinct, it makes more sense to blame me than global warming.

#5. Staghorn Coral: False again! We are told by the U.S. government that the Staghorn Coral is one of the most important corals in the Caribbean,[319] which is suffering from (1) excessive fishing, which means there are fewer fish to keep the reefs clean by eating the plants, and (2) human pollution that dirties the clear waters where corals can thrive."[320]

#6. The Orange-Spotted Filefish: If you would like to prove that these fish are not extinct, send $50 to Blue Zoo Aquatics and buy one.[321]

This article from a Google search falsely claimed the extinction or impending extinction of all six of its featured animals. It is consistent with what Mark Twain told us when he wrote, "The reports of my death have been greatly exaggerated." This misinformation is irresponsible propaganda intended to make us worry about imaginary problems. It is consistent with threats from the U.N. that a third of all species could be extinct within 50 years.[322] This is a pattern of junk science with perhaps a bit of dishonesty.

Predictions by Al Gore from *An Inconvenient Truth*

In *An Inconvenient Truth*, Al Gore warned us of 16 animals that were destined for extinction. None of these seem to be following his warning: many are thriving, and most of their troubles relate to overfishing, overhunting for their fur or feathers, or a desire for exotic pets. These problems are amplified by human pollution and expanded agricultural or commercial development. Here is an update on Gore's extinct animal list:

- The **White-Fronted Goose** has a global population of about 3 million, and its extinction rating assigned by the International Union of Threatened Species is of Least Concern.[323] [324] [325] [326]

- **Giant Glass Frogs** are listed as critically endangered on the IUCN Red list.[327] They have become popular in the international pet trade and sell for significant prices.[328] Climate change does not appear to be their major problem.[329]

- **Greater Mouse Lemurs** are also captured as exotic pets. Their natural habitat in the Madagascar woodlands is also threatened by the severe loss of trees.[330] [331]

- The **Macaroni Penguin** is extremely prolific, with an estimated population of 11 million.[332][333]

- The **Coqui Tree Frog** has become invasive, with concentrations of about 20,000 frogs per acre in Hawaii.[334][335] For Al Gore to learn more about the Coqui Tree Frog situation, he should do what Hawaiians do: Call Pest Control at the Hawaii Department of Agriculture at 643-PEST-ORG.[336]

- The **Antarctic Fur Seal**[337] is believed to be the most abundant species of fur seal and is rated of Least Concern by the IUCN.

- The **Wattled Crane** is the tallest flying bird native to Africa and is classified as Vulnerable.[338][339] The biggest problem for cranes is a major reduction in their wetland habitats due to increased human agriculture and industrialization.[340][341]

- The **Yellow-Eyed Penguin** is considered Endangered.[342][343] These animals are very rare, and their numbers have been dwindling, primarily because of being caught and drowned in the nets of commercial fishing trawlers.[344][345][346][347]

- The **Red-Breasted Goose** has a population estimated at 70,000. Extensive human agricultural growth forced them to move from the Caspian Sea to more suitable habitats in Bulgaria and Romania.[348][349][350][351][352]

- The **Grey-Headed Albatross**[353] is the world's largest bird. During the 19th century, about 5 million albatrosses were killed for their feathers.[354] The Albatross is classified as Endangered even though every year, 1 million fly to the Midway Atoll's Wildlife Refuge and  National Memorial.[355] The albatross's current major problem is being accidently killed by Japanese fishermen.

- The **Bowhead Whale**[356][357] "Like most whales, it was hunted nearly to extinction."[358] The Center for Biological Diversity reports that the Bowhead Whale "should be an Endangered Species Act success story." Following the prohibition of commercial whaling, this population grew to 10,000.[359] Bowhead Whales are listed as of Least Concern by the IUCN.[360]

- The **Leopard Seal**[361] is the second largest species of seal in the Antarctic and has never been exploited. The estimated population of the Leopard Seal ranges from 220,000 to 440,000.[362] The Australian

government and the IUCN have both declared that the extinction of
the Leopard seal is of Least Concern.[363]

- The **Emperor Penguin**[364] is the largest penguin and is endemic to
  Antarctica.[365] There are about 3 million Emperor Penguins.[366] [367]

- **The Golden Toad**, as described above, is extinct[368] and has been extinct
  since 1987 (20 years prior to Gore's book.)[369] Clearly, Gore was tardy in
  his prediction.

Conclusion

Climate Activists give us a list of animals claimed to be headed toward
extinction, which, upon closer inspection, are thriving or would thrive if
humans didn't hunt them or destroy their habitats. Global warming has
nothing to do with their survival. As Shakespeare had Caesar explain it to
us, "The fault, dear Brutus, lies not in the Stars, but in ourselves. We are
the underlings."[370]

In conclusion, we should not fear, worry, or feel guilty about global
warming because polar bears, whales, seals, penguins, geese, and other
species have not been driven to extinction by the 1°C warming of the past
century, and there is no scientific data supporting predictions that any of
them will perish from global warming in the future. We have every reason
to believe we are lucky to be living on Earth at a time when these animals
thrive and provide a diversity of life that exists nowhere else.

Chapter 4 Quiz

	True	False
1. Polar bears are dying of exhaustion because so much ice has melted, and they must now swim longer distances to find food.	☐	☐
2. The population of polar bears is plummeting because of global warming.	☐	☐
3. Global warming has turned the oceans from basic to acidic, harming marine life.	☐	☐
4. Once damaged, coral reefs take centuries to recover, and many never will.	☐	☐
5. Rising water temperature and acidity are the major causes of harm to coral reefs.	☐	☐
6. You can trust Google to find the most reliable information on animal extinctions.	☐	☐
7. Global warming is a major factor in the impending extinction of many endangered species.	☐	☐
8. Al Gore correctly predicted that global warming would cause 16 species of animals to become extinct.	☐	☐
9. Global warming in Antarctica is threatening the survival of the emperor penguin.	☐	☐
10. The best way to protect endangered species is to join the fight against global warming.	☐	☐

The answers to all of the questions are False. Here's why:

1. Al Gore's claim that polar bears are dying because they cannot swim far enough to find food has been debunked. Polar bears thrive in areas where ice melts fast.

2. Between 1970 and 2015, the polar bear count has increased from about 10,000 to over 20,000.

3. A pH of 1 to 7 is acidic and above 7 to 14 is basic. Pure water has a pH of 7. The oceans and seawaters fluctuate between 7.8 pH and 8.3 pH and average about 8 pH.

4. The Palau reefs were badly bleached in 1998 and had "turned to rubble." But by 2012, the rubble had made remarkable recoveries, and "brightly colored coral varieties [were] growing ... where the water was more acidic than anything predicted for ocean acidity levels 100 years from now." (See page 72)

5. The major causes of bleaching and other damage to coral reefs are tourism, trash, sediment from nearby developments, and ingredients in sunscreen.

6. The featured article in a Google search falsely claims global warming is causing the extinction of six species of animal, yet none of them is extinct or threatened by global warming.

7. The most common threats to endangered species are hunting, destruction of habitat, capture for sale as pets, and natural causes.

8. Gore was wrong on all 16 animals. None are threatened by global warming, and most are flourishing.

9. There are about 3 million Emperor penguins in Antarctica, and they live in large colonies of 5,000-10,000. There currently is no risk of extinction.

10. Fighting global warming is probably the least effective way to protect endangered species. Conservation efforts should focus on protecting and restoring habitats and ending hunting and poaching.

FAKE NEWS: CODE RED! In 2018, there was a large international meeting of the world's Seals. Unanimously, after significant discussion, they voted that the polar bear lobby had biased all liberal universities, governments, and media against them. They decided to wage a major campaign about the Fake News that polar bears can only survive by eating seals. The campaign will promote polar bears eating other animals in the future, including reindeer, seabirds, waterfowl, and whale carcasses.

Summary

- The 1°C increase in temperature has not hurt a single polar bear.
- The world's coral reefs are not endangered by climate change.
- All the Activists' animal extinction claims are based on shoddy science and are debunked by real-world data.
- There is no wave of climate-caused animal extinctions we should fear, worry, or feel guilty about. It is simply not happening.

Chapter 5
Predictions

"No matter who you are, or how smart you are, or what title you have, or how many papers your side has published, if your prediction is wrong, your hypothesis is wrong."

(Richard Feynman, Nobel Prize winner in Physics, 1965)
Or simply put: "*Garbage in; Garbage out.*"

The author exposes the outstanding flexibility of the Climate Activists who have, with great vigor, predicted we will either die of freezing or heat exposure due to climate change; Activist predictions have almost always been wrong because Nature has refused to cooperate with them; Activists aggressively defend their poor predictions with fear and insecurity; and several leading Climate Realists have completed multiple, major scientific studies based on history, empirical knowledge, and guided by significant integrity.

Global Cooling between 1944 and 1976

Before the current concern about global warming, the world's Activists worried about global *cooling*. In the 1970s, the prevailing belief was that the Earth was sentenced to another Ice Age. Because much of this history has been scrubbed from the internet, Google provides very little information about which experts predicted a global cooling crisis. For example, Paul Ehrlich, Stanford Professor, was perhaps the leading proponent of global cooling, but you will have to look very hard into the internet to find information on his statements of support that a global cooling disaster was inevitable.[371] [372]

In a 1958 article titled *The Coming Ice Age,* Betty Friedan tells us that this is *A True Scientific Detective Story* that features Maurice Ewing of Columbia University and William Donn, a meteorologist, who stated, "The world is now heading into another Ice Age. It will come not as a sudden catastrophe, but as the inevitable culmination of a process that has already begun."[373] The conclusion to their *True Scientific Discovery Story* is that we should be worried about freezing. Kenneth Watt, a University of California (Davis) professor, was another global cooling activist. He predicted the Earth would be 4 degrees cooler by 1990 and 11 degrees cooler in 2000. He said, "this is about twice what it would take to put us into an ice age."[374] The National Aeronautics and Space Administration (NASA) claimed that by 2020, fossil fuel burning could cause global temperatures to drop by 6°F.[375]

Between 1944 and 1976, the Earth's average surface temperature declined,[376] even though atmospheric CO_2 levels were rising.[377] In Figure 35, the **blue line** is global carbon emissions in billion metric tons, the **solid red line** records deviations (or "anomalies") from the long-term average global temperature, and the **dotted red line** shows the downward trend.

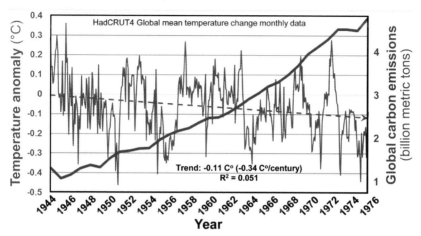

Figure 35: Rising CO$_2$ Emissions and Falling Global Temperatures from 1944 to 1976 [378]

Knowing that there was global *cooling* hysteria before there was today's global *warming* hysteria is important to understanding our current climate debate. Just as happened in the 1970s, many prominent scientists, celebrities, and the media now fan public fears with scary headlines and failed predictions. The 1970s climate experts assumed the global temperature before 1944 was the best or ideal temperature for everyone on the planet, and a lower temperature would necessarily produce more harm than benefit. Everything is the same today, except now the Activists assume today's temperatures are ideal and anything *warmer* will harm us.

Temperature Predictions 1988 - Current

The conversion from fears of global *cooling* to fears of global *warming* took about a dozen years and became popular about 1988. You already know that the Earth experienced only 1°C of warming during the last 140 years, but the U.N. and most U.S. academics predict a much larger temperature rise in the near future.

Currently, many Americans believe that global warming is the major climate change problem. Historically, three Activist thought leaders that have guided this belief are (1) James Hansen and his 1988 global warming predictions, (2) Michael Mann's Hockey Stick of 1998, and (3) the U.N. IPCC's continuous pronouncements of global warming disaster.[379]

James E. Hansen, the director of NASA's Goddard Space Center in the 1980s,[380] published an article in *Science* in 1987 predicting that burning fossil fuels would increase global temperatures by around 3°C by 2020.[381] [382] He was wrong, but his projections were highly influential at the time, and the media, government, and most universities supported him. Hansen is only one of many U.S. government experts who started out with accurate historic U.S. government data and then produced projections based on bias and faulty computer projections.

In 1988, Hansen wrote an article and advised the U.S. Senate that there was a "high degree of confidence" that "a cause-and-effect relationship" would generate major global warming. His predictions included what he called "Scenario A business as usual."[383] [384]

Figure 36: Hansen's Most Probable Prediction:[385] **Scenario A
And Actual Temperature Increases from 1985-2020. (HadCRUT4
and UAH6)**

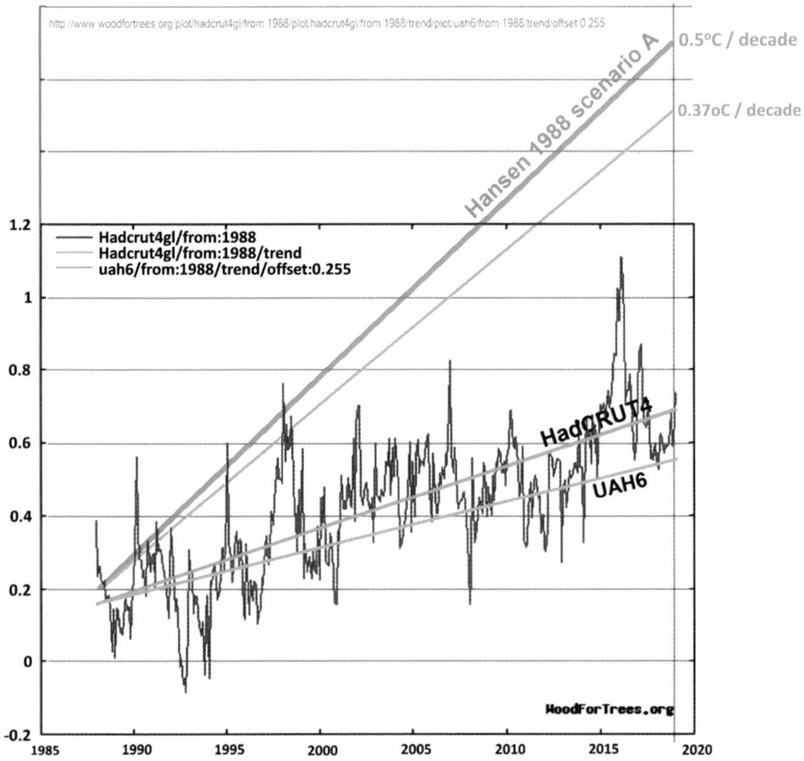

In this chart, Hansen's "Most Probable" Scenario A,[386] the Dark Green line proves that Hansen's projections overestimated the modest global warming of subsequent years; the actual warming is in **Red.** [387 388] Hansen's prediction of temperature increase was wrong by more than three times as real temperature change has been minimal. Hansen misled Congress and the nation into believing global warming was a crisis. Despite his inaccurate prediction, the mainstream media still reports that Hansen's prediction was "mostly correct"[389] - a good example of how the mainstream media, guided by the Activists, are mostly wrong in their warnings about climate change disasters.

Michael Mann's Hockey Stick is the most famous of all charts related to global warming.[390] Mann, now a professor of atmospheric science at Penn State University, was only a recent Ph.D. graduate when he published his Hockey Stick chart in 1998. Mann based his chart on selected tree-ring widths. His depiction of the Earth's temperature changes over 1,000 years included the disappearance of known temperature variations such as the Medieval Warm Period (900-1300) and the Little Ice Age (1300-1850). It showed temperatures increasing since about 1900. Since Mann's work supported fears of run-away global warming, it was quickly embraced by the Activist global warming movement and featured in IPCC reports.

Figure 37: Mann's Hockey Stick Graph [391]

Variations of the Earth's surface temperature

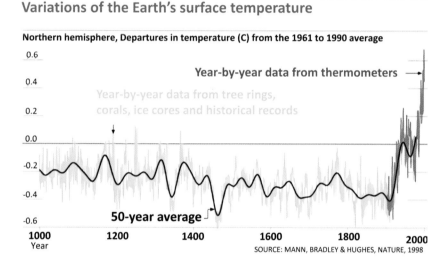

SOURCE: MANN, BRADLEY & HUGHES, NATURE, 1998

Code:

Blue = Range; Black = 50-year averages; **Red = Projected, The Hockey Stick**

Mann's Hockey Stick temperature increase prediction of 1998 was followed by 18 years of *cooler* weather, as shown in Figure 38. [392]

Figure 38: Global Temperatures 1998-2015
(1998 was warmest year)[393]

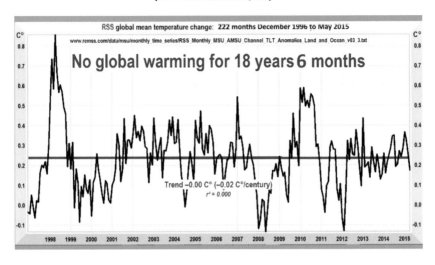

One would have thought that Mann might have allowed his Hockey Stick to die a quiet death, but, ignoring his mistake, Mann wrote a book in 2012, *The Hockey Stick and the Climate Wars*, to defend his position.[394] Numerous scholars disputed Mann's findings, but they were shunned, ignored, censored, and even slandered in a rush to embrace climate alarmism.[395] His leading critic was a Canadian, Steve McIntyre, who accused Mann of "poor data handling, obsolete data and incorrect calculation(s)," producing a result that could not be scientifically replicated.[396]

Climate Activist Catastrophe

During the past 50 years, Activists have bombarded us with conflicting warnings about whether we should be frightened by heat or cold, but always they tell us climate change is a catastrophe. Virtually all scientists agree that global temperatures increased during the past 100 years by about 1°C. Activists have told us multiple times that there are less than 12 years before global warming will cause a climate change catastrophe. It seems to me that a more accurate and truthful prediction has come from *The Babylon Bee*, a satiric publication: "Experts warn we have only 12 years left until they change the timeline on global warming again."

Here are examples of predicted climate change catastrophes:

- The EPA published a paper in 2013 entitled *"Moving Forward with incorporating 'Catastrophic' Climate Change into Public Policy."*[397]

- NASA reported in 2016 that the "Earth is warming at a pace unprecedented in 1,000 years."[398]

- NASA reported in 2018 that "we have received a warning that global warming will destroy life as we know it."[399]

- Science magazine in 2016 warned us, "Climate catastrophe? A half a degree warming could make the difference."[400]

- The Guardian in 2021 reported, "The climate disaster is here – this is what the future looks like."[401]

Global Warming Projections

The U.N. IPCC, the world's leading Activist group, relies on an average of 102 climate models programmed to predict Earth's rising surface temperature. All of the models predicted too much warming, so naturally, the IPCC's average did, too. The chart below may look a bit complicated, but you will get the point.

Figure 39: 102 Climate Models that All Get It Wrong [402]
(For 45 years, Activists have overstated projected Global Warming) [403]

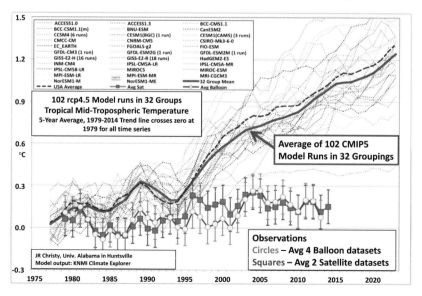

The **blue** squares show Earth's average near-surface temperatures from 1979 to 2016 based on highly reliable satellite data (NASA). The green circles show weather balloon data for the same period. You can see that these two databases, which represent actual observations, closely match. This is real Earth data based on real science (satellites and balloons). The **red** line, on the other hand, shows the average of about 100 computer models used by the U.N. IPCC. [404] [405]

The chart above is an excellent example of how Climate Activists have produced consistently inaccurate global warming projections. This is shoddy science. Why is that? Could it be that their computer projections include a biased component blaming human contributions to climate change? I know that if I were to strike out 100 times in a row, I would consider changing my position. Why don't the Climate Activists?

Both the Activist and Realist scientists acknowledge that atmospheric CO_2 contributes to increasing the Earth's surface temperature. The major areas of disagreement are (1) to what extent, and, if any, will there be global warming?; (2) should we be worried about it?; and (3) should we try to do something about climate change? The Realists would say that global warming is minimal, that there is nothing to worry about and nothing to do about it.

Most of the Activists at the U.N. IPCC (and NASA and the NOAA) predicted a 1.5°C to 4°C increase between 1990-2100. [406] [407] This is significantly higher than the past 100 years, where the total increase was 1°C. As Kevin Trenberth, previously the lead modeler at the National Center for Atmospheric Research (NCAR), stated, "(None of the) models correspond even remotely to the current observed (global climate)." [408]

Perhaps worst of all is that the Activist scientists don't practice science. They don't consider why, during the past 100 years, there has been no acceleration of sea levels, no increase in hurricanes, and a reduction in fires which is historically what happened. They don't consider the possibility that our climate might have been amazingly stable during the past 100 years. Instead, they offer us their certainty of catastrophe and gloom as the WSJ reports, "Their most recent projections of future global warming are still dire."[409] A typical Activist comment is "(It will) worsen storms, intensify rainfall, boost sea-level rise - and cause more extreme heat waves, droughts …crop failures and the spread of infectious diseases."[410]

Activist Predictions and Empirical History

In addition to making predictions about future temperatures, Climate Activists predict the effects of higher temperatures on everything from people and other animals to plants, glaciers, fish, coral reefs, forests, and more. Many illustrations have been detailed in past chapters. The following is a brief recital of climate change predictions that we now know were false. There are many more than this, but I think this is enough to make my point:

- **Climate Refugees** – In 1989, an Associated Press article said if we don't stop global warming by the year 2000, entire nations will be wiped off the face of the Earth due to sea-level rise.[411] In 2005, Climate Activists predicted 50 million people would be displaced by rising sea levels between 2000 and 2010.[412] In 2020, they claimed some 3 billion people would likely have to move in the future to avoid rising temperatures.[413]

  Reality – No nation has disappeared due to rising seas. Sea levels continue to rise at the same slow rate of the past 100 years. People don't move just because the temperature is one or two degrees warmer than a century ago. Europe has had static population, while the population of Africa, the warmest continent, has grown four-fold in just the past 40 years.[414] These facts are contrary to the "climate refugees" prediction.

- **Economic Impacts** – Activists predict rising global temperatures will cause global gross domestic product (GDP) to fall by at least 10 percent.[415]

  Reality – There has been GDP growth for 100 years in all capitalist countries, large and small, including Burkina Faso, the world's warmest country.[416]

- **Heat Waves** – Activists predict heat waves will become more numerous and deadly due to global warming, with some claiming this already occurred between 2015 and 2019.[417]

  Reality – There are no more U.S. heat waves now than there were in 1900.[418] The number of days with temperatures above 100°F has fallen in the United States.

- **Poles and Glaciers** – Activists predict ice at the North Pole and South Pole is melting so fast that water levels will rise many feet and destroy almost every coastal city.[419] [420] In 2009, Al Gore predicted the Arctic Ice Cap would disappear by 2014.[421] In 2008, *The Guardian* predicted the Arctic would be free of sea ice by 2018.[422]

  Reality – The North Pole may be slowly losing ice mass, but the South Pole is gaining ice.[423] Arctic sea ice, as of August 2020, covered 2 million square miles.[424] Glaciers have been slowly shrinking, but they've been doing that ever since the last Ice Age.[425] It has been estimated that melting ice contributes about 1mm/year (1 foot/ 300 years) to global sea-level rise.[426]

- **Ocean Acidification** – Activists claim an increase in acidity of about 0.1 pH units since the beginning of the Industrial Revolution and predict acidity will increase 0.3 to 0.4 units, (100-150%) by 2100. [427] They warn us that ocean acidification poses a measurable threat to the health of all marine species and will devastate fisheries.

  Reality – Oceans are alkaline (basic) and not acidic, with an average pH of about 8. During the past 100 years, the pH of the oceans has fallen by a fraction of Activist predictions and at current rates, it will take thousands of years for ocean acidity to reach a level where it could negatively affect marine life.

- **Coral Reefs** – Climate Activists predict coral reefs and their beautiful colors will disappear in 20 years.[428] [429]

  Reality – Historically, there has been bleaching and loss of reefs for the past 400 years, long before human CO_2 could have been a factor.[430] Coral reefs are endangered more by human trash, agricultural run-off, and sunscreen lotion than by global warming.[431] In some places, like Palau, the strength, diversity, and beauty of the coral reefs are higher where the pH is lower.[432] [433] Variability and resiliency, not stability, have characterized coral reefs for thousands of years.

- **Hurricanes and Tornadoes** – Climate Activists predict hurricanes and tornadoes will become more frequent and more intense and cause more damage, leading to, among other things, more mental disease.[434] [435] [436]

  Reality – The frequency of land-falling hurricanes and tornadoes in the United States has not increased during the past 100 years, and the frequency of both actually fell during the past 50 years.[437] [438] [439]

- **Forest Fires** – Climate Activists tell us that global warming has already and will continue to dramatically increase the number and size of forest fires.

Reality – The global magnitude of forest burning has not increased[440] nor has the acreage burned by forest fires.[441] The vast majority of forest fires are caused by human actions such as arson, carelessness, and power lines.[442] [443]

- **Droughts** – For the past 50 years, Activists have predicted more droughts around the world. They predicted the United States would have to ration water by 1974.[444] [445]

  Reality – About 75% of the most severe droughts occurred during the early part of the past 120 years[446] , and more than 300,000 square kilometers of arid soil is now greener than 30 years ago.[447] [448]

- **Floods** – Activists predict widespread flooding along coastlines as sea level rise continues to accelerate.[449] [450]

  Reality – There has been no evidence of sea-level rise acceleration during the past 100 years. Subsidence, the ground sinking because of development or removal of groundwater, often contributes to coastal flooding. The historic sea level rise has been about 1 foot during the past century.[451] [452] [453] [454]

- **Polar Bears** – Activists predict global warming will cause the extinction of polar bears. They maintain that melting ice forces polar bears to swim longer distances to find food, which results in exhaustion and drowning.[455]

  Reality – Actual polar bear studies between 1970 and 2020 verify a rise in population from about 10,000 to about 30,000.[456] [457] [458] The greatest threat to polar bears has not been global warming but hunters that shoot them.

- **Other Animal Extinctions** – Activists predicted in 1970 that by 1985 all-important animal life in the sea would be extinct.[459] [460] In 2014, they predicted one-third of all species could be extinct by 2070[461] and that more than one million species would become extinct if fossil fuel emissions were not quickly reduced.[462] Al Gore identified 16 species that he claimed would become extinct.

  Reality – Gore was wrong on all 16 animals. Most exist in large quantities, including the Bowhead Whale,[463] [464] the Leopard Seal,[465] [466] the White-Fronted Goose,[467] and Emperor Penguin.[468]3Fewer than 1% of the 850 species on the list of most endangered species have become extinct during the past 30 years.[469]

Litigation

What do you do if you are a Climate Activist and want to permanently prevent any future disagreement? Lawsuits seem to be one answer! Activists have formed the Climate Science Legal Defense Fund, a group devoted to attacking those who disagree with them.

In 2011, Mann filed a libel claim against Dr. Timothy Ball, a distinguished Canadian climatologist (now retired), claiming that Ball made false and defamatory statements inferring that Mann was guilty in association with an alleged "Climategate" scandal. Mann sought damages, an injunction against further similar statements, and permanent removal from all media relating to these statements.

In June 2019, Mann lost the suit, paid court costs, and issued an apology.[470]

In 2012, Mann sued the Competitive Enterprise Institute (CEI) and *National Review* for defamation over an article comparing him to Penn State coach Jerry Sandusky. The CEI blog post stated, "Instead of molesting children, [Mann] has molested and tortured data in the service of politicized science." The case was dismissed. Mann Lost.[471]

In 2015, Hansen's granddaughter and 20 other minors sued the U.S. government, claiming it has failed to do enough to confront the "growing, mortal threat of global warming" and is violating the youngest generation's constitutional rights to life, liberty, and property.[472] To my knowledge, the internet is silent on any results of this lawsuit.

As you would expect, the gold standard of companies the Activists want to sue is Exxon, the world's largest oil company. Over the years, Exxon engaged many experts to study climate change and published 50 papers on climate-related research, sometimes pointing out that the politics of climate change pose a potential risk for investors. Those reports were often peer-reviewed. Nevertheless, in 2015, Sheldon Whitehouse, a U.S. Senator, and Eric Schneiderman, New York's Attorney General, cited these studies and sued Exxon under the Martin Act, a 1921 New York law enacted to prosecute stock-sale-boiler rooms.[473] Exxon handed over millions of pages of documents in response to subpoenas. In 2019, the court ruled in favor of Exxon, finding the company did not mislead its investors or anyone else by its actions.[474]

The Climate Realists

Climate Realists[475] use historical and empirical data to support their conclusions. Sometimes, Activists call these people "climate skeptics," which is accurate since they are skeptical of Activist warnings of climate change disasters. But more often, they call Realists "climate deniers" or "science deniers," which is pure slander. No one "denies" that the climate changes. Anyone with a conscience should admit that "denier" is a pejorative name used to cast Climate Realists into the same camp as Holocaust Deniers. That's a shameful distortion of language and a personal attack.

Activists prove the weakness of their arguments when they attack opponents personally. They use personal attacks, rather than facts or scientific support, because their arguments are weak. As is explained below, many of the Climate Realists are eminent scientists. The following is a short description of a few of the world's leading Realist scientists, information rarely available in a book on climate change: [476] [477]

- **H. Sterling Burnett, Ph.D.**, is managing editor of *Environment & Climate News* where recent articles have clarified that the polar bears are doing well, that climate change is not causing extreme weather, and that hurricane costs have not increased.[478]

- **Myron Ebell** is a leader at the Competitive Enterprise Institute (CEI). Ebell's writings confirm that computer models have predicted significantly more warming than has occurred; future large sea-level rise claims have no legitimate scientific basis, and surface temperature data has been manipulated.[479]

- **Christopher C. Horner, J.D.,** Senior Legal Fellow at CEI, has been criticized by Michael Mann for "orchestrating the attacks on climate scientists … through vexatious and frivolous FOIA demands."[480] But Horner is only doing what the mainstream media has failed to do: investigate fraud and incompetence in government agencies such as EPA and NOAA and expose the corruption inside the global warming movement. He has authored several books, including, *How Global*

Warming Activists Use Threats, Fraud, and Deception to Keep You Misinformed (2008).

- **Bjørn Lomborg, Ph.D.,** is president of the Copenhagen Consensus Center (CCC) and has been cited as one of "the 10 most-respected global warming skeptics." In 2021, he wrote a series of articles in the Wall Street Journal explaining why the world isn't doomed by climate change, why we are safer from climate disasters than in the past, that many more people die from cold as die from heat and that the amount of land burned has declined steadily since 1900. [481]

- **Steve Milloy, J.D.,** is the publisher of JunkScience.com, a website devoted to exposing the shady science relied on by EPA and other government agencies to make environmental policy. His books include *Green Hell: How Environmentalists Plan to Control Your Life and What You Can Do to Stop Them* (2009) and *Junk Science Judo: Self-defense Against Health Scares and Scams* (2001).

- **Lord Christopher Monckton** is a science writer who created the mathematical puzzle Eternity.[482] Activists have called him a "famed idiot" whose "scientific credentials are listed on a grain of salt"[483] and "Lord of the Lies." In fact, he's a mathematical genius whose work on climate science has appeared in peer-reviewed scientific journals. His writings explain why human influence on sea-level rising is minimal; why it makes no sense to panic over the climate; the chaotic behavior of climate models; and restrictions on free speech relating to climate change. [484] [485] [486]

- **Marc Morano** hosts ClimateDepot.com and exposed many problems relating to the Climate Activist movement in a 2016 film, *Climate Hustle.* He has been called "the central cell of the climate-denial machine" and the "Climate Change Misinformer of the Year."[487]

- **Matt Ridley, Ph.D.,** is author of *The Rational Optimist, How Innovation Works,* and *Genome: The Autobiography of a Species.* He also has written several articles challenging the belief that resource depletion is an issue of importance and was the editor in 2002 of *Best American Science Writing* (Harper Collins).[488]

- **Willie Soon, Ph.D.,** is an astrophysicist and a geoscientist at the Harvard-Smithsonian Center for Astrophysics. He is the author of hundreds of articles about climate change appearing in many of the world's most prestigious science journals. His discoveries challenge computer modelers and advocates who consistently underestimate solar influences on cloud formation, ocean currents, and wind that cause the climate to change. At the Ninth International Conference on

Climate Change in 2014, Soon accepted the "Courage in Defense of Science Award."

- **Anthony Watts** is a meteorologist, a senior fellow with The Heartland Institute, and the founder and host of WattsUpWithThat.com, a highly popular website on the climate. His work on climate issues, specifically the problems with temperature measurements, has been cited worldwide in books, studies, and government reports.

- **Gregory Wrightstone** is executive director of the CO_2 Coalition, a nonprofit devoted to providing education on the contributions made by carbon dioxide to our lives and the economy. Attacked by Activists many times, including by Willard McDonald, who claims Wrightstone "Is tricking the reader with his sleight-of-hand logic" and his errors "are so blatant …that it's clear he is being willfully deceptive."[489] Wrightstone is the author of *Inconvenient Facts: The Science that Al Gore Doesn't Want You to Know,*[490] [491] which was a #1 Best Seller in Amazon's climate category.[492]

These Realist scientists are attacked every day for writing and telling the truth. How irritating and unfortunate! They hardly ever receive support from the media, the government, or educational institutions but they are persistent and brave in defending, explaining, and following empirical science and history. As Thucydides, the world's first major historian, told us in 500 B.C. in the *History of the Peloponnesian Wars*, "We study the past as a key to the future." It is unfortunate that the Activists don't.

Real News: Almost always, we are bombarded with Fake News from the Activists. For a change of pace, here is real news about a few major improvements for humanity during the last 50 years of global warming:

- Life expectancy has increased by over 25%
- Extreme poverty has been reduced by about half
- Total food costs have decreased by 40%
- Literacy has increased by 50%
- Air pollution has sharply declined

There will be no quiz in this Chapter. Everybody gets an A. These are participation awards.

FAKE NEWS: CODE RED! It was only through significant due diligence that I was able to learn the truth behind this *True Scientific Detective Story:* You remember how, during the 2020 Pandemic, multiple Climate Activists determined that now was an opportune time to alert Americans and Canadians about the imminent polar bear extinction due to climate change. Through government funding and the support of the *New York Times* and the *Washington Post*, the Activists distributed free to all citizens a booklet proving the near-term extinction of polar bears.

By happenstance, several wayward copies went to the literate polar bear population, who understandably became concerned. The booklet failed to mention that the Canadian government was still allowing the native Inuit to kill 6,000 polar bears every decade.[493] [494] Also, they wanted the Activists to stop telling the world that the polar bears were victims of global warming because the small temperature change did not affect them; instead, since the 1970s, when laws were passed against shooting them, the polar bears were thriving.[495] [496] They had four more requests: (1) Stop taking money from uninformed citizens to save the polar bears; (2) tell citizens not to worry because they were *not* drowning; (3) understand that the slightly warmer climate did not bother them; and (4) leave them alone to enjoy their polar bear freedoms.

My final comment on this *True Scientific Detective Story* was that in the November election, 85% of the polar bears voted against Activist candidates. The defeat was so bad that the Climate Activists decided to concentrate on their claim about the imminent disappearance of all coral reefs because, as everyone knows, corals can't vote.

———————————

Summary

- Virtually every major prediction of climate disaster by the Climate Activists has been proven wrong and should be ignored.

- The ideas of the Climate Realists, who follow real environmental science, should be studied and respected.

Chapter 6

Energy

As an additional benefit to the reader, the author will discuss the importance of fossil fuels, explain why industries make great efforts to reduce their use of fossil fuels, and identify some significant problems with renewable energy technologies. The author will also present reasons why the fossil fuel alternatives such as wind and solar power will have great difficulty achieving their growth goals. To better educate the Activists, the author explains why we use fossil fuels and then challenges the reader to name one Activist who has identified a unique benefit provided by fossil fuels.

The chapter also clarifies why almost all major energy companies and individuals work hard to reduce their carbon footprint primarily because there is an "invisible hand" that encourages them to make money and try to please customers and allows them to apply their limited resources on other stuff. The author has also provided some additional facts related to fossil fuels and energy which do not relate to climate change. He recommends you read this anyway and consider this bonus knowledge provided to you at no extra cost and confirmation that his book is a bargain. This chapter may also enable you to impress your friends by explaining to them words many are not familiar with, like "terawatt," which could lead them to offer to buy you lunch the next time you meet.

Fossil Fuels: The Sole Source for a Plethora of Products

In addition to generating energy, fossil fuels are needed to produce a myriad of products, including plastics, foods, health and beauty aids, and other products. Wind and solar energy cannot produce these products, meaning their manufacture would be impossible in a world without fossil fuels.

- **Plastics:** Almost all plastics are derived from natural gas, a type of fossil fuel. They are versatile, durable, lightweight, and cheap. Without fossil fuels, there wouldn't be any cell phones, iPads, desktop computers, or remote controls. I will bet the Activists hadn't thought of that. Plastics are essential for medical devices such as IV bags and syringes; car components including dashboards and airbags; housing for electronics, toys, and plastic furniture.

- **Health and Beauty Aids:** These include nail polish, soaps, shampoos, toothpaste, detergents, body lotions, face creams, deodorants, sanitary products, contact lenses, cough medicines, dentures, heart valves, and anesthetics.

- **Fertilizers and Food Products:** Products derived from fossil fuels include ammonia, nitrogen and potassium fertilizers, liquid pesticides, packaging materials that keep foods fresh, chocolate ingredients, food preservatives, and chewing gum.

- **Other:** Without fossil fuels, we wouldn't have the asphalt used to pave roads; the synthetic organic pigments in paint; carpets made with nylon or polyester; ballpoint pens; acrylic or polyester fabrics; synthetic rubber for tires, basketballs, crayons, leggings and pantyhose, toilet seats, and balloons.

It is unfortunate that so many Americans have developed a bias against fossil fuels due to media, educators, and government claims that fossil fuels are destroying our climate and so few reminders of the enormous contributions that fossil fuels make every day to our economy. The next time someone tells you we need to stop drilling for oil or end all coal mining, ask them if they want to stop using toothpaste and deodorant and drink with paper straws for the rest of their lives.[497]

Fossil Fuels

Endlessly, the Activists lecture us that the continued use of fossil fuels will inevitably lead to disaster.[498] In January 2022, Sarah Kaplan and John Muyskens wrote an article about climate change in the *Washington Post* (which is important because, in a typical month, the *Washington Post* has over 50 million unique readers). In the article, the authors tell us that the past 7 years were the 7 "hottest in recorded history," that 2021 temperatures were a bit over 1oC higher than 1880; and that 2021 recorded the hottest temperatures in 25 countries. This was confirmed by NASA, NOAA, and Berkeley Earth. For the Pacific Northwest, 2021 was "a disaster so severe that it would have been virtually impossible in a world without climate change." [499] [500]

And as you have probably guessed, the claimed cause of this disaster was "the burning of fossil fuels," which has "irrevocably changed the planet."[501] In the article, Zeke Hausfather of Berkeley Earth tells us that we have an "extremely clear trend of very high temperatures."[502] Also, John Cook has told us, "If we keep burning fossil fuels the way we are now, more than 40% of species could go extinct by the end of the century."[503]

However, you know from carefully reading previous chapters in this book that the years from 2017-2021 have been cooler than 2016; that humans can hardly distinguish a one-degree temperature difference (polar bears probably can't either); that more people die from cold than heat; and that there are fewer days over 100 degrees than during the last century. So why are the Activists so worried when the impact of fossil fuels has been so minimal? Are they arrogant, forgetful, misleading, biased, ignorant, or dishonest?

Why do the Activists so confidently tell us that 30 years from now, fossil fuels will cause a disaster when we have so little ability to accurately forecast even a few months of weather? For example, NOAA predicted that Virginia would be warmer than average during the winter of 2021-2022, with no unusual heavy snow.[504] But, at the end of January 2022, Virginia had about 2 feet of snowfall,[505] and thousands experienced many hours stuck in their cars, partially due to this poor weather forecast.[506]

Why We Use Fossil Fuels

We burn fossil fuels mainly to produce energy, and we use this energy to produce electricity, power transportation, and enable the industry to provide products and achieve its goals. These activities are necessary to feed, house, and meet the other needs of 330 million Americans. We desire as a nation not just to survive but thrive.

The chart below shows how the sources of energy are connected to their uses. Note that electrical power, transportation, and industry represent about 90% of all energy use. The left side shows that 80% of total energy is sourced from fossil fuels (petroleum [oil], natural gas, and coal); the right side identifies the magnitude of each of these activities.

Figure 40: How Global Energy Production is Used [507]

U.S. primary energy consumption by source and sector, 2017
Total = 97.7 quadrillion British thermal units (Btu)

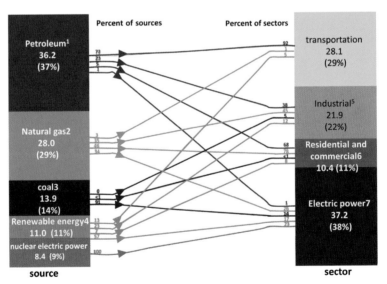

Let me acknowledge that the following sections on the uses and sources of energy are a bit dry, but they are important to understanding how successful efforts by industry and technology reduce fossil fuel use. As a reader, you may find this section useful as a summary of the different types of energy sources and uses. If you choose to skip this section, feel free to go to the section on death by fossil fuels which you might find more interesting.

Technology

In 1950 our economy used 15,000 BTUs to produce $1 of Gross Domestic Product (GDP), and by 2010 we only used 5,000 BTUs to achieve the same result.[508] [509] Here are some examples of how technology has contributed to using energy more efficiently.[510]

Electric Power Generation: The U.S. generates and consumes about 4 trillion kilowatt hours (kWh) of electricity per year.[511] The largest use is producing electricity, which consumes 37% of all energy. Improvements in the electric power grid include increased efficiency of the generating sources, higher voltage equipment, flexible alternating current transition systems, computerized monitoring protection control, grill grid management, and energy efficient load management.[512] These improvements have enabled American consumers to save about 2.4¢ per Kilowatt hour,[513] which represents about 20% of total cost. [514]

It appears that we have two choices to improve the electric grid: Either allow industry to continue making gradual improvements or have the Federal Government put in a low-carbon electricity grid at a cost of about $5 trillion ($5,000,000,000,000). Your share of the additional government debt would be over $15,000. [515]

Your choice!

Transportation: This is the second largest user of primary energy, consuming approximately 28% of total U.S. energy. During 2019 about 1.5 million metric tons of atmospheric CO_2 resulted from gasoline and diesel fuels. In addition, 150 million metric tons of CO_2 emissions resulted from corn ethanol and biomass which are excluded from CO_2 measurements because the politically strong Activists have defined these as "environmentally friendly" energy sources.[516] The fact that ethanol produces more atmospheric CO_2

than fossil fuels per pound is excluded from its measurement, and is an example of shoddy science created, promoted, and enforced by the Activists.[517] Doesn't this sound like a political decision?

- **Gasoline Cars:** During the 15 years prior to 2018, average automobile fuel economy increased from 20 to 25 miles per gallon (mpg), while new cars used 2% less gasoline/year.[518][519][520] One reason for the improvement was that decreasing steel and increasing plastics (which are made from fossil fuels) decreased the weight of the cars.[521][522]

- **Electric Cars:** Although they require less energy when in use, electric cars generate about 20% more greenhouse gases (GHG) during their production.[523] Even after traveling 100,000 miles, a typical electric car will have produced more atmospheric CO_2 than a gasoline car because the electric car doesn't save energy until it has been driven approximately 130,000 miles.[524]

- **Trucks:** During the 45 years prior to 2018, technology improvements in U.S. light-duty trucks saved more than 50% of fuel that would otherwise have been consumed by the sector. During the 10 years prior to 2017, 17 billion tons of CO_2 were saved because truck mileage increased from 5.9 to 7.3 mpg.[525] Since large trucks use about 20% of all transportation fuel, this efficiency saved 4% of all energy consumed by the transportation sector. It is anticipated that truck mileage may soon be increased to 10 mpg through additional technology improvements.[526][527][528]

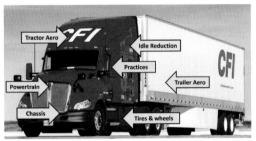

How Trucks Save Fuel

- **Planes:** Airplanes produce about 12% of all U.S. emissions and generate 3% of global atmospheric CO_2. During the past 60 years, the number of airline passengers increased by 40 times to over 4 billion/year, and fossil fuel usage/mile dropped by 75%. Technology improvements include denser seat configuration, improved engines, higher passenger loads, enhanced aero-dynamics, and lighter materials.[529] During 2020, commercial aircraft use dropped 60%,[530][531] but, as confirmed below, there was no change detected in the world's global warming or climate change.

Industrial: This sector includes facilities and equipment used for manufacturing, agriculture, mining, and construction and uses about 22% of all energy.[532] Most industrial greenhouse gases are generated by burning fossil fuels for manufacturing, food processing, mining, chemical processes, iron and steel, and cement production.[533] [534] For economic reasons, virtually every industry has attempted to reduce its energy consumption, as in the datacenter example below.

Datacenters: The largest industrial electricity users are datacenters which currently in the U.S. use about 416 terawatts of power. They account for about 3% of global energy use, which is projected to increase to 14% by 2040.[535] [536] Power is required by datacenters because almost all computers have fans and motors which must be cooled with air-conditioning.

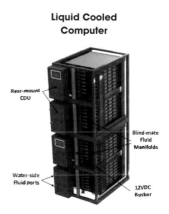

Liquid Cooled Computer

Today's technology can eliminate up to 95% of the fossil fuels used in datacenters by using single-phase dielectric liquids, which can conduct heat away from the hot electronic components, thus eliminating the need for air-conditioning and repurposing the heat generated by computers for heating water.

Figure 41: Liquid Cool Computers Will Reduce Datacenter Carbon Footprint [537]

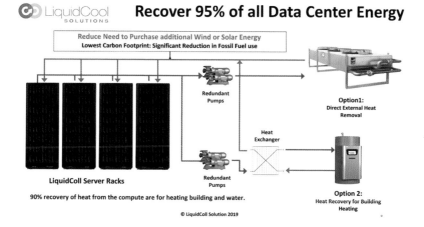

Agricultural: Recent technology improvements that have reduced the carbon footprint include more efficient fossil-fuel based fertilizers,[538] energy efficient, low methane dairy motors, [539] [540] drones that make surveying irrigation systems, soil conditions and apply water and herbicides more precisely;[541] and no-till farming that allows seeds to be efficiently "drilled" into the soil.

Residential and Commercial Applications: This sector uses 11% of energy. The residential sector includes homes and apartments; the commercial sector includes offices and stores. The two major uses here are heating and cooling equipment, which have experienced continuous energy improvements for 40 years.[542] [543]

Commercial Applications

Tankless Water Heaters: One example of an energy-saving device used in a growing number of businesses and homes is the tankless water heater. During the past decade, tankless water heaters have been developed, which save over 30% of energy compared to traditional products. For example, the average hotel using tankless water heaters saves about $13,000 yearly. Other advantages include instantaneous and endless hot water, lower installation costs, lower operating and maintenance costs, corrosion elimination, and reduction in space requirements.

Figure 42: Technology and Energy Saving in Water Heaters[544]

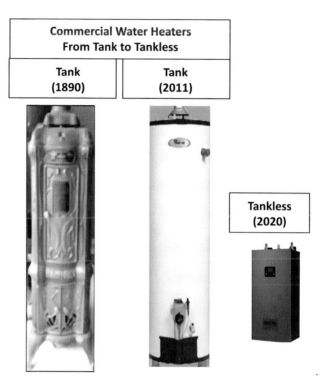

What is clear is that all major energy users have this in common: They are continually developing technology to save energy (and money). What do almost all of the Activist media have in common? They don't mention the significant industry successes in saving energy! Why not? The media has little interest in informing us about good news. Instead, as Charlie Chester of CNN explains: "Fear Sells."[545]

Sources of Energy: The following chart shows the relative sources of energy. You will note that fossil fuels (oil, gas, and coal) provide about 80% of all energy. Electricity generated with fossil fuels has an average cost of about 5¢/ kilowatt hour (kWh). Renewables fluctuate in costs: hydroelectric is about 3¢ /kWh; solar has about 12¢ /kWh; and wind ranges from 7¢ to 15¢ /kWh.[546 547]

Figure 43: Sources of Energy [548]

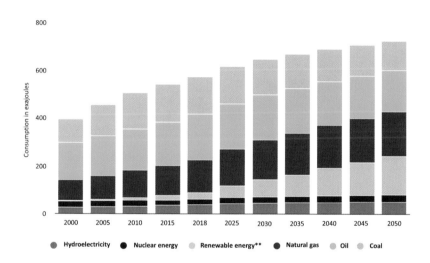

The chart below may be easier to read. It also shows how fossil fuels provide 80% of all human energy needs. Nuclear power 6%, Renewables 7%.[549 550 551]

Figure 44: Sources of Global Energy [552]

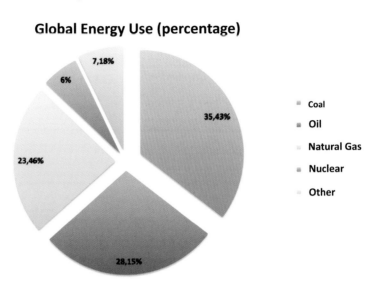

Global Energy Use (percentage)

7,18%

6%

35,43%

23,46%

28,15%

- Coal
- Oil
- Natural Gas
- Nuclear
- Other

Hydroelectric Power (Hydro): Hydro produces about 7% of total U.S. electricity generation[553] and is most commonly used where there is a high concentration of water that has a large vertical drop (i.e., Niagara Falls).[554] [555] The U.S, which uses less than 20% of its potential hydroelectric power,[556] has a program called the "Hydropower Vision," which would increase our use of hydro by 50 gigawatts by 2050.[557] Perhaps people feel that hydro is boring "old technology," which justifies the press concentrating the majority of its efforts on wind and solar energy, but since hydro is the least expensive of all alternative energies, it does seem that more support and media coverage could be of benefit to all.

Nuclear Energy: Accounting for 6% of U.S. electricity generation,[558] nuclear energy has no carbon footprint and has been an efficient source of energy in the past; however, newer generations will likely be more expensive than the past low-cost technologies.[559] Nuclear accidents have been rare and current technology makes future accidents even more improbable. However, these infrequent accidents are very costly, and disposing of nuclear waste, even with advanced technologies, can be expensive.

Although several experts have advocated replacing fossil fuels with nuclear energy, both economic and emotional concerns will determine its future use, which is why nuclear energy is expected to have a low future growth rate. France, the largest nuclear energy user, has obtained 75% of its electricity from nuclear energy and has had no accidents in 30 years.[560] The absence of nuclear energy is a major reason why Germany's per-capita emissions have been 10 times greater than France's, while the cost of energy in France is about 40% less than in Germany, which relies heavily on renewable energy.[561] [562]

Figure 45: Per-Capita CO_2 Emissions in Germany and France, 2016 [563]

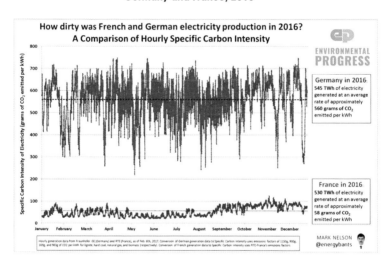

Although the U.S. will not be producing any more nuclear energy in the foreseeable future due to safety worries, China has completed the world's first small modular nuclear reactor and expects to spend over $400 billion on nuclear energy during the next 15 years.[564]

Wind Energy: Even the staunchest supporters of wind energy will acknowledge that killing between 50 million and one billion birds each year is a serious detriment.[565] [566] Last year 150 bald eagles were illegally killed by Nextera for which it was fined $35 million.[567] In 2020, there were about 68,000 wind turbines in the U.S[568] and almost 400,000 worldwide.[569] [570] Wind energy requires lots of space: Two 260-foot-diameter turbines must be separated by about 1/3 of a mile.[571] At least 500 square miles would be needed to service the entire U.S.[572] A single 100-megawatt wind requires 30,000 tons of iron ore, 50,000 tons of concrete, and 900 tons of non-recyclable plastics.[573][574] The turbines have a lifespan of 12 to 20 years, depending on location,[575] and when their useful life ends, there are significant removal costs.[576]

Biomass: Consisting of wood, chips, sheets, pellets, firewood, and charcoal, Biomass is a source of energy that accounts for about 1% of U.S. electricity.[577] Trees and plants remove about 30% of all CO_2 emitted by humans.[578] A typical hardwood tree absorbs about 45 pounds of CO_2 yearly or about 1 ton in 40 years.[579] Since trees and plants take in CO_2 for photosynthesis, planting lots of trees would reduce atmospheric CO_2. In 2020, the Trillion Tree Act was introduced but did not pass in Congress to supplement solar and wind energy as part of the "Global Climate Change Program."[580] Since it would take over 1000 years to plant 1 trillion trees (800 million trees x 1000 years = 800 billion trees), it is only political mathematics that enables anyone to make the Trillion Tree claim. Proponents claimed there is room for these trees in our open spaces and that the cost would total about $5 billion a year.[581] It is hard to believe that wood should be considered an environmentally sustainable solution because burning huge quantities of wood will destroy forests and increase atmospheric CO_2.[582]

Crescent Dunes Project (Nevada) https://www.canadianmanufacturing.com/technology/nevadas-110-mw-crescent-dunes-solar-project-goes-fully-online-162871/

Tonopah (190 miles NW of Las Vegas)
Photo: SolarReserve

Solar Energy:

Objections to solar-based energy include the fact that so many birds have been fried by solar projects.[583] For example, the 110-megawatt Crescent Dunes solar energy facility in Nevada redirected concentrated solar energy to a point 1,200 feet above the ground and ignited 130 birds in mid-flight within one hour.[584] Also, solar panels require many toxic chemicals, including lead, cadmium, telluride, gallium, copper, indium, hexafluoroethane, and polyvinyl fluoride.[585]

Renewables: Some Additional Thoughts

Even after 20 years of implementation and billions of dollars of subsidies, wind and solar provide less than 15% of our energy needs.[586] The addition of solar and wind energy and the reduction of other electricity sources will lead to numerous blackouts of electricity during the next several years: According to NERC, it is likely that two-thirds of the U.S. will experience blackouts due to the reduction of energy sources other than wind and solar.[587] For example, Michigan expects blackouts due to the closing of its clean energy nuclear power plant, which produces more electricity than all the wind and solar power in the state.[588]

Because solar panels collect energy only when there is sun and wind turbines function only when there is wind, their energy must be stored with expensive and relatively inefficient batteries. Tesla's battery factory in Nevada is the largest battery factory in the world, and it would require 500 years to store one day's supply of U.S. energy.[589] [590]

If you consider the total cost of energy, lifespan, storage systems, maintenance, fuel costs, decommissioning, and subsidies, solar and wind cost four times other competitive energy sources. Only by ignoring these factors can one falsely claim that solar and wind operates at lower costs than fossil fuels. Regarding subsidies, solar gets ten times the subsidy of fossil fuels.[591]

The Sun

Many times, in discussing our energy needs, we forget about the importance of the sun. We all know the sun is hot, but how hot? The temperature varies from approximately 15 million degrees Celsius (27 million degrees Fahrenheit) at its core to 5,500 degrees Celsius (10,000 degrees Fahrenheit) at its surface.[592] NASA tells us that "Every 1.5 millionths of a second the sun releases more energy than all humans consume in an entire year."[593] Certainly the sun is generating thousands of times more heat than fossil fuels.[594] Activist scientists almost always minimize the enormous heat contributed by the sun and overemphasize the impact of fossil fuel emissions.

Figure 46: Almost Constant Energy from the Sun for 400 Years [595]

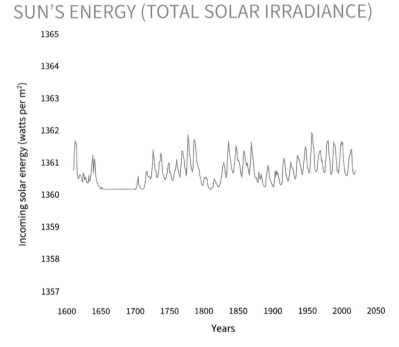

I thought you might be interested in viewing a historical shift in world energy use. Asia increased its share of worldwide energy use dramatically between 1980 and 2013, as shown on the next page.

Figure 47: Worldwide Energy Use[596]

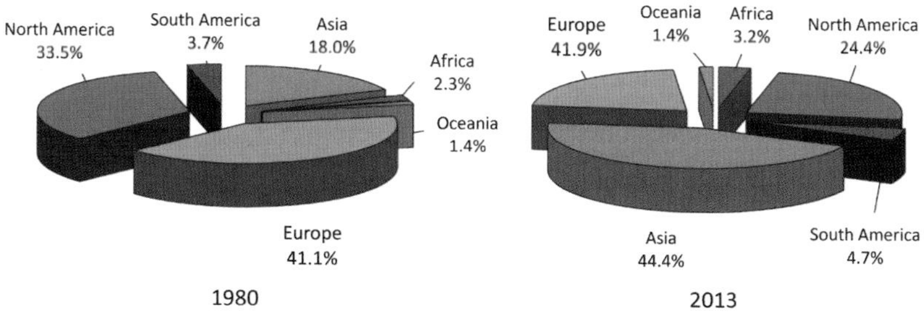

North America 33.5% South America 3.7% Asia 18.0% Africa 2.3% Oceania 1.4% Europe 41.1%

1980

Europe 41.9% Oceania 1.4% Africa 3.2% North America 24.4% South America 4.7% Asia 44.4%

2013

Death by Fossil Fuel

It should be no surprise to learn that the Climate Activists claim that fossil fuels cause air pollution, which, in turn, causes death by many diseases, including heart disease (the #1 cause of death in the U.S.)[597] But, did you know that the Activists claim that fossil fuels, through air pollution, are killing more than the number of people murdered in homicides? Well, believe it or not, a leading Harvard professor led a study of death by fossil fuel and found that in the U.S. there are about 350,000 fossil fuel murders[598] [599]compared to 25,000 homicides.[600] Thus, the claim is that fossil fuels are more than 10 times more lethal than guns!

Before examining the validity of the 350,000 deaths by fossil fuels, let's acknowledge that the quality of air in the U.S. has significantly improved during the past 40 years. The EPA maintains statistics on air pollution, and during 1980-2020, their studies show that the reduction in air pollutants has been enormous while, for example, the number of miles traveled in cars and trucks during that time frame increased enormously (by 70%). Since 1980, all major air pollutants have been significantly reduced, including carbon monoxide, lead and sulfur dioxide (by over 80%), nitrogen oxides (by over 60%), and Ozone (by over 30%).[601] Cleaner air prevents thousands of premature deaths, reduces heart attacks, reduces hospital visits due to child asthma attacks, and prevents lost school and work days.[602] Current air pollution consists mostly of particulates (referred to as PM2.5 below), which are tiny particles and Ozone[603].

The Activists at Yale CC, using advanced computers (and their imagi-nations), claim that "Burning fossil fuels creates harmful air pollution that can worsen… heart disease."[604] So let's look at air pollution in the U.S. and its impact on heart disease deaths.

Figure 48: # of Days of Air Pollution by City during 2020 [605]

The **Red bars** show the 10-year average of days with high air pollution (referred to as *unhealthy days*). The standard measurement for reporting deaths is to identify the number of deaths per 100,000 people, and the U.S. currently reports that, on average, there are 210 heart disease deaths per 100,000.[606]

The chart above clearly shows that Los Angeles has had the worst air pollution in the U.S and has had over 1,100 bad pollution days during the past 10 years, which is more than twice as much as any other major U.S. city. For the Climate Activists to have any credibility for their claim of deaths by fossil fuels, the number of heart disease deaths in Los Angeles must be much higher than in any other U.S. city. But Los Angeles has fewer heart disease deaths than the U.S. average (190 per 100,000).[607] [608] This should be compared to New Orleans, which had only 80 high pollution days over the past 10 years and 200 deaths per 100,000 from heart disease,[609] and Philadelphia, with 220 air pollution days (1/5 of Los Angeles) and 205 deaths per 100,000 (more than Los Angeles). [610]

Thus, there is absolutely no correlation between fossil fuels causing air pollution and deaths by heart disease in the U.S. It is only the creativity, imagination, and highly biased advanced computerization of the Activists that could even conceive of 350,000 deaths in the U.S. from fossil fuels. Based on the information on high pollution days in America, the Activist claims of massive deaths by fossil fuels should be considered **FAKE NEWS**.

Conclusion

It is unlikely you will find confirmation in the *New York Times*, the *Guardian*, or CNN that fossil fuels have any merit or that improving technology significantly reduces our use of fossil fuels. Major media almost always tells us that fossil fuels must be banned. The good work that industry does must remain invisible!

There are good reasons for more efficiently using energy which would reduce our dependence on fossil fuels, including that (1) we can save money and spend that money on other human needs, and (2) they exist only in a finite supply. But fossil fuels are currently abundant, inexpensive, safe, and ideally suited to generate electricity. For transportation, where fossil fuels are essential, solar and wind are useless. The environmental damages that wind and solar energy cause should not be ignored, and their weakness in producing only intermittent energy should be considered in their evaluation. The reality that there are not enough resources on Earth for renewables to supply our total energy needs is rarely mentioned by Activists.

Chapter 6 Quiz

	True	False
1. Almost all uses of fossil fuels produce atmospheric CO_2, which causes global warming.	☐	☐
2. Because fossil fuels are so inexpensive, there is little cause to remove them from industrial applications through technology.	☐	☐
3. The cost of energy has increased dramatically during the past 70 years, which is why it is essential that we reduce our dependence on energy.	☐	☐
4. Because there has been so little improvement in transportation efficiency, it is essential that we reduce our dependence on cars, trucks, and planes.	☐	☐
5. The rapid increase in energy consumption by datacenters is one reason we need to develop alternatives to fossil fuels.	☐	☐
6. Industrial, residential, and agricultural uses of fossil fuels are all growing at exponential rates, which will certainly increase global warming.	☐	☐
7. The only meaningful non-fossil fuel alternative energies are wind and solar.	☐	☐
8. Because Germany uses primarily wind and solar energy for its non-fossil generation of energy, it is more energy efficient and has lower electricity costs than France, which relies heavily on nuclear power.	☐	☐
9. Solar and wind energy are the ideal solution to our energy needs because they are less expensive and have almost no adverse environmental effects.	☐	☐

All of the answers to the Quiz are False. Here's why:

1. Fossil fuels are essential for the manufacture of many products, including plastics, asphalt for roads, pesticides, and health and beauty aids, for which, in many cases, there are no alternatives.

2. Fossil fuels are expensive and reducing commercial use of fossil fuels saves money and increases profits. Lower prices improve customer satisfaction.

3. Energy costs have dropped significantly during the past 70 years. In 1950, our economy used 15,000 BTUs to produce $1 of Gross Domestic Product (GDP), and currently, it requires only 5,000 BTUs.

4. During the 15 years prior to 2018, average automobile efficiency increased from 20 to 25 miles per gallon. During the past 10 years, truck technology increased average truck mileage from 6 to 7 miles per gallon. Energy use by planes dropped 75 percent during the past 60 years.

5. Datacenter technologies, including liquid cooling, have the capability of reducing energy consumption by 60% to 95% compared to air-cooled datacenters.

6. 6. Virtually every aspect of industrial, residential, and agricultural use of fossil fuels is currently being addressed technologically to reduce energy needs.

7. Major non-fossil fuels which have proven to be both effective and inexpensive include hydroelectric power (water) and nuclear energy, both of which require no fossil fuels and generate no atmospheric CO_2.

8. Electricity costs in Germany are 40% higher than in France.

9. Although costs have decreased, wind turbines and solar energy currently still cost more than fossil fuels. Environmental issues include the need for large quantities of rare-earth and hazardous materials; large energy needs for manufacturing and disposal costs, and significant land requirements.

FAKE NEWS: CODE RED! For this edition of FAKE NEWS, I want to provide you with both sides of a FAKE NEWS controversy and ask you to decide which is fake. In 2020, the Activists claimed that the movie *Planet of the Humans*, by Michael Moore, was FAKE NEWS. The movie described the change in focus from a purely environmental movement concerned with conservation to promoting wind and solar energy, which the movie concludes were no better than fossil fuels.[611]

A typical Activist comment was: "Their misleading, outdated, and scientifically sophomoric dismissal of renewable energy is perhaps the most dangerous form of climate denial, eroding support for renewable energy as a critical climate solution."[612] Another review said the movie is a gift to "big oil" while "deceiving viewers about climate change."[613] As you would expect, an opposing view was *"Planet of the Humans* does an excellent job exposing the environmental impacts of [renewable energy]."[614] Initially, the movie was censored by Climate Activists but is now readily available. When you have a couple of hours, I suggest you watch it on Amazon Prime, and decide for yourself whether this is FAKE NEWS or a realistic evaluation of renewable energy.

Summary

- Without fossil fuels, we will destroy our ability to meet our energy needs. The reduction in availability of fossil fuels is a major cause for blackouts.

- Without fossil fuels, we would lose thousands of products, including plastics, computers, phones, TVs, numerous health products, and paints.

- Businesses continually work to reduce fossil fuel use to save money.

- Windmills and solar panels kill millions of birds, require large amounts of rare elements and poisonous chemicals, and, when total costs of storage are included, wind and solar cost much more than fossil fuels.

- Fossil fuels are not causing air pollution in the U.S., where our air is cleaner than in the past.

Chapter 7
Current Events

"Life is solitary, poor, nasty, brutish and short."
(Thomas Hobbes 1588-1679)

This comment is surprisingly similar to the warnings of the Climate Activists if the Earth becomes one degree warmer than it is now (The Paris Accord).

In which the author explains that the huge reduction in fossil fuel use during the 2020 COVID-19 pandemic did not reduce global warming; that the majority of money anticipated for use in the Green New Deal (GND) has nothing to do with climate change; and those predictions of the Earth's destruction should we fail to meet the goals of the Paris Accord contradicts the past 100 years of historic reality.

The author also explains why the demands for action and the warnings by the Climate Activists of what must be done today to avoid climate catastrophes should be ignored and stopped.

Finally, to justify these hugely expensive and unnecessary programs which solve non-existent problems, let's look again at the unrealistic projections of the Climate Activists, which they use to justify crisis behavior.

2020 and COVID-19

In 2020, we experienced the worldwide COVID-19 pandemic that reduced fossil fuel usage by more than any other single event in world history. Causes for this reduction included closed factories, decreased auto and air travel, and the shutting down of most of the world's major economies. Fossil fuel usage was down 17% by early April 2020.[615] During 2020, the International Energy Agency predicted that total 2020 global CO_2 emissions would drop by 8%[616] and world fossil fuel use would drop by 9%.[617] Meanwhile, actual gasoline usage during 2020 dropped more than 10%.[618]

Climate Activists are demanding that we reduce our use of fossil fuels, and in 2020 human civilization did just that. So, what was the environmental effect of this worldwide reduction of fossil fuels? We should have seen smaller temperature increases and possibly fewer of the bad weather events attributed to climate change.

Temperature: Let's look for temperature changes due to reduced fossil fuel use.[619] Guess what? There was no meaningful change in temperature, as verified by the CICR in Norway, which reported a meaningless reduction of 1/500 of 1°C. [620 621 622] The large reduction in energy use produced no visible effect on global temperatures.

Figure 49: There Has Been No Global Warming for Five Years[623]

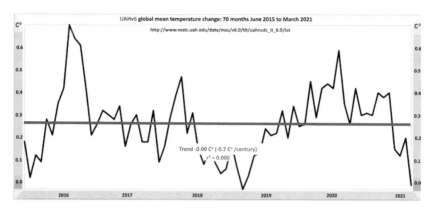

Climate Change: Let's look at hurricanes and forest fires in 2020:

- **Hurricanes**: showed no reduction during 2020. Hurricanes were stronger and more frequent than normal. There were over 25 tropical storms. Meanwhile, there were 10 tropical cyclones which, on average, were more intense. These storms were supported by a La Niña that developed in the summer months of 2020.[624] By comparison, during 2021, when there was a substantial increase in fossil fuel use, there was a *reduction* in tropical storms. This result is contrary to the Climate Activists' theory.[625] [626] [627]

- **Forest Fires:** also showed an increase during 2020. There were a number of major forest fires in the Western U.S. (including California, Oregon, and Washington), and about 8.2 million acres burned.[628] [629] The largest single forest fire in recorded history was the "Doe Fire," which was part of the "August Complex" fire, where about 1% of California burned.[630] During the first 11 months of 2021, there were about the same number of wildfires and significantly fewer acres burned than in 2020 according to the National Interagency Fire Center.[631] All of these facts are contrary to the Climate Activists' theory.

Conclusion: The pandemic resulted in significant reductions in CO_2 but had no effect during 2020 on temperature or improvement in the weather. 2020 had a very active hurricane season and many major forest fires, including the largest fire in California history. There is no evidence that the significant reduction in CO_2 caused by human reaction to COVID-19 had any impact on climate change or weather improvement.

Government and the Green New Deal (GND)

During the past 30 years, an international consensus has developed among most governments that the major crisis of our time is climate change and that it is our fault because we cause global warming. In this book, you

have seen many scientific studies showing that global warming has been minimal; however, there are many anticipated future government programs that will extensively attack this non-problem. To keep it simple and save time, I will concentrate on only two major climate change programs: The Green New Deal (GND) and the Paris Agreement.

In February 2019, U.S. Rep. Alexandria Ocasio-Cortez (AOC) and her less-famous partner, Sen. Ed Markey, presented The Green New Deal (GND). This was a "massive policy package" that would "eliminate all U.S. carbon emissions." AOC told us, "Even the solutions that we have considered big and bold are nowhere near the scale of the actual problem that climate change presents to us."[632]

Non-Climate Change GND Expenses: Most of the expense of the GND has nothing to do with sustainability, environment global warming, or climate change. Instead, most funding for the GND will support the redistribution of wealth, universal health care, increased minimum wages, job guarantees, food, housing security, and social justice initiatives.[633]

Green New Deal Programs That Do Not Address Climate Change

	Estimated Cost[634]	Estimated Cost Per Household
Guaranteed jobs	$6.8 trillion to $44.6 trillion	$49,000 to $322,000
Universal health care	$36 trillion	$260,000
Food security	$1.5 billion	$10

So, why does the GND, a program claimed to address global warming and climate change, include such huge expenses for programs that have nothing to do with climate change? Why would most of the money in the *GND* be spent on "free" health care, guaranteed jobs for everyone, and free food. Clearly, these topics have nothing to do with global warming or climate change, but they represent over 80% of the GND program.

I believe the answer, and one that would be agreed upon by all sides of the political spectrum is that adding these climate-irrelevant programs are 99% Progressive/Socialist politics! By including these programs, the Progressives/ Socialists make a giant step toward eliminating private health insurance and achieving their universal government health care objectives. These would be difficult to achieve without hiding it in legislation that includes claims of global warming and climate change. Although polls show that many Americans would like to have every citizen covered by a government health care system,[635] [636] [637] only a tiny minority (10%) want to abolish private health care insurance.[638] And of course universal health care would not produce fewer hurricanes, tornadoes, floods, or climate extremes.[639]

Green New Deal (GND) Programs Related to CO_2 Reduction:

- The GND would require a transition to a low carbon energy electricity grid with zero-emission energy sources and renewable energy. The smart power grid, according to the Electric Power Institute, would cost about $40 billion per year for 10 years ($400 billion).

- Electric cars and high-speed rail systems would replace or reduce air travel and cars that use gasoline.

- Improving the energy efficiency of all homes and industrial buildings to state-of-the-art energy efficiency would cost about $250 billion per year for 10 years ($2.5 trillion).[640]

- Research toward the deployment of advanced technologies.

GND Programs Related to CO$_2$ Reduction [641]

	Estimated Total Cost	Estimated Cost Per Household
Low-carbon electricity grid	$5.4 trillion	$39,000
Net zero emissions transportation system (i.e. electric cars and high speed rail)	$1.3 trillion to $2.7 trillion	$9,000 to $20,000
Guaranteed green housing	$1.6 trillion to $4.2 trillion	$12,000 to $30,000

The GND will not solve a problem or have any meaningful global warming effect:

- What is the justification for spending trillions of dollars to solve a problem that does not exist? Why spend any money, time, and effort on such a useless endeavor?

- Previously, you have seen that the reduction of atmospheric CO$_2$ during the COVID-19 pandemic had virtually no effect on global warming or climate change during 2020. Bjørn Lomborg estimated that the GND program would reduce temperature increases by about 1/20 of one degree.[642] The costs, according to Lomborg, would be about $1.5 trillion per year and an additional $42 trillion in debt by the end of the century.[643] As Winston Churchill told us, "Politicians can tell you what the future will be and afterwards why it did not happen."

The Paris Agreement

Signed by almost 200 countries in 2016[644] and re-signed by the U.S. in 2021, the key environmental goal of the Agreement is to prevent temperatures from rising more than 1.5°C above that of the base year 1840 (the year selected as the start of the industrial era). The Paris Agreement calls for preventing temperatures from rising 2°C above 1840 temperatures, which Climate Activists have determined would be a catastrophe.[645] Thus, a 1 1/2°C increase is acceptable, but 2°C above 1840 temperatures is not. The claim is that this difference of 1/2°C from current temperatures will cause climate catastrophe.[646]

The Paris Agreement specifically rejected this additional increase of 1/2°C because it was found "not to be in line with the ultimate goal of the Convention;"[647] [648] and "will destroy the planet as we know it."[649] These Climate Activist experts have claimed that to meet the Paris Agreement's goals for emission standards,[650] greenhouse gases must be reduced by 7.6% per year for the next decade, and we must achieve net zero emissions during the second half of the 21st century.[651] [652] [653]

Although all Climate Activists are positive that this 1/2°C difference[654] will destroy the Earth, they have not agreed upon the date at which this catastrophe will take place. Some Activists claim the date demanded by the Paris Agreement is 2050, while others believe that 2100 is the correct date.[655] [656] Although they do not agree on the disaster date, they fully agree that this 1/2°C difference will cause disaster!

The Paris Agreement Bias

Any efforts by the U.S. to reduce emissions will be offset by China and India, as shown in the next two figures. Both are concentrating on growing their economies, enabling their people to become wealthier, and have no interest in wasting money trying to control the climate.[657] [658] [659] [660]

Figure 50: China and India Past Increase in Coal Production[661] [662]

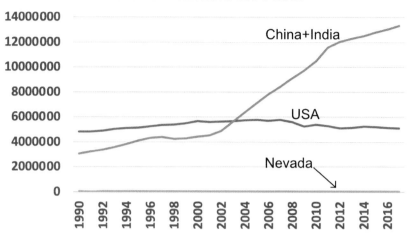

Figure 51: Future Increases in Coal Consumption & Production[663] [664]

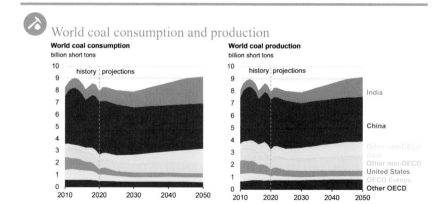

Can you tell the difference?

I believe that it is almost impossible for a human being to distinguish a temperature difference of 1°F (1/2°C). The next time you are driving with a friend, close your eyes, let your friend adjust the temperature in your car by 1°F, and guess if the temperature was increased or decreased.

Historically, there is absolutely no example of such a small change causing any large disruption. On the other hand, during the past two days, the temperature in Milwaukee fluctuated between 40°F and 10°F. I can assure you that any Realist and Climate Activist person could tell the difference.

Predictions:

The disaster predictions caused by a 1°C increase contradict past reality: The Climate Activists' justification for the Green New Deal and the Paris Agreement is that if we do nothing now, the world's climate will cause civilization to disintegrate. They tell us that an increase of 1°C from today's temperature will result in more hunger, poverty, and shorter lives. Therefore, it makes sense to review what have been the changes in food availability, wealth, literacy, and length of life during the past when temperatures increased.[665] Let's see if there is any justification for such negative predictions by noting the following information.

Gross Domestic Product (GDP):

Figure 52: Wealth and CO_2 Emissions 1900-2010

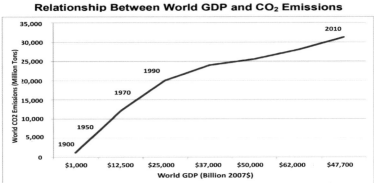

Source: U.S. Energy Information Administration, International Energy Agency, U.S. Bureau of Economic Analysis, and Management Information Service, Inc.

The chart above shows that as carbon dioxide has increased in the atmosphere, the world GDP has risen.

The following chart shows that GDP has increased during the thirty-year span between 1990 and 2019, a period when CO_2 emissions increased almost every year. One exception was in 2009, when emissions decreased. According to Climate Activist theory, a decrease in CO_2 should show an increase in GDP. It is interesting that the one year between 1990 and 2019 which showed a decrease in GDP was 2009, a year when CO_2 emissions worldwide dropped by 100 million tons.[666] In summary, during the past 120 years, there has been no scientific or empirical support for the claim that GDP will drop in the future with more atmospheric CO_2.

**Figure 53: U.S. Gross Domestic Product (GDP)
Growth 1990-2019** [667]

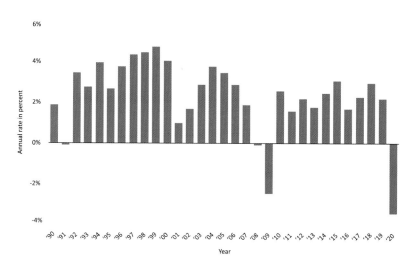

Perhaps it is a coincidence, but 2009 was the sole year between 1990 and 2019 where GDP decreased, and 2009 was the rare year that both fossil fuel use and CO_2 dropped (100 million tons), a fact contrary to the Climate Activist theory. [668] [669]

Poverty: Using $1.90/day as the current definition of poverty, between 1985 and 2015, the share of global population living in poverty declined from over 40% to under 10%, as the World Bank chart below illustrates.

Figure 54: Reduction in Absolute Poverty [670]

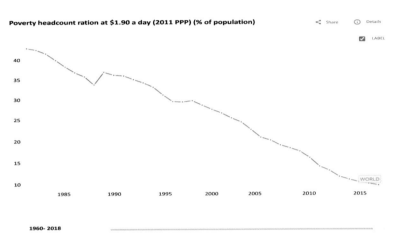

Education and Literacy: At the beginning of the industrial revolution, before the increases in CO_2 and temperature, only 20% of the world's population was literate. Now, more than 80% can read.

Figure 55: Rising Literacy Around the World, 1820-2010 [671]

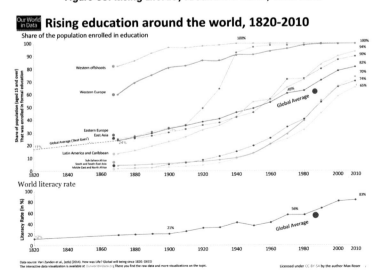

Length of Life: "The dramatic increase in average life expectancy during the 20th century ranks as one of society's greatest achievements," [672] notes a report from the National Institute on Aging, a division of the National Institute of Health.

Figure 56: Life Expectancy in the U.S. 1960-2020 [673]

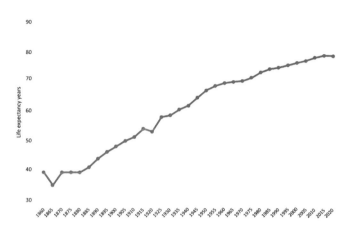

Cost of Food: The cost of food in the U.S., measured as a percentage of per-capita income, fell nearly 50 percent from 1860 to 2010. [674 675]

Figure 57: % of Per-Capita Income Spent on Food in the U.S. [676]

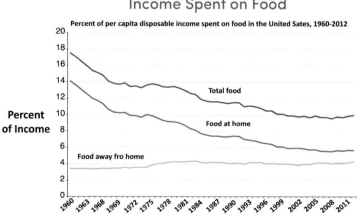

Income Spent on Food

Percent of per capita disposable income spent on food in the United Sates, 1960-2012

Historical Realities vs. Future Unrealities

As previously described, the remarkable improvement in human existence has coincided with our effective use of fossil fuels. You will recall from an earlier chapter that Thucydides, the Greek historian of *The Peloponnesian Wars,* told us "We study the past as a key to the future." If the past is an indication of the future, then a small increase in temperature should have no negative effect on humanity. Although the Climate Activists tell us that our future will be significantly worse than the past, when we investigate their specific claims, we find an almost total lack of validity.

Carbon Dioxide and Global Warming: The IPCC at the UN, the major influencer to The Paris Agreement, has predicted an increase of 500 ppm in CO_2 levels in 80 years. This is a multiple of past increases:[677] (6 ppm/year compared to the current increase in CO_2 of 2.4 ppm/year.[678]) According to Anna Scapiro at the University of Pennsylvania, this huge growth of atmospheric CO_2 will impair our mental faculties,[679] a conclusion contradicted by EPA studies which show no negative effect of CO_2 on human health.[680][681] As you know, global temperatures since 2016 have declined. In fact, during the 30 years before 2021, world temperatures increased by an imperceptible 0.13°C.

Willie Soon, the Harvard astrophysicist, has calculated that even if we were to achieve zero net carbon emissions by 2050, we would only reduce world temperatures by .05°C.[682] This is 1/10th of the mandatory .5°C degrees required by the Paris Agreement.

The Oceans, Sea Levels and the Flooding of the Coasts: The *Guardian*, a Paris Agreement supporter, tells us that "The last time the world was 2°C above pre-industrial levels was 15 million years ago during the Miocene period when … sea levels rose some 40 meters (125 feet) higher than today"[683] and that higher sea levels will make almost half of humanity become refugees by 2100 [684] However, you know from Chapter 2 that there are *no* sea disaster refugees and the sea levels have risen only 1/8 inch/year for 100 years.

Drought: The *New York Times,* a strong supporter of the Paris Agreement, reported in 2018 its "good news" that if we can hold the temperature increase to ½°C, only 350 million will suffer from drought; but an additional 60 million will suffer if we hit 1°C.[685] You probably recall from Chapter 2 that we have fewer droughts now.[686] Meanwhile, the Earth has become greener during the past 30 years as we have 300,000 square kilometers fewer of arid soil.[687]

Figure 58: The Earth Is Greener than 40 Years Ago [688]

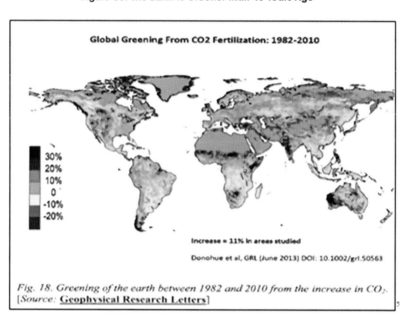

Global Greening From CO2 Fertilization: 1982-2010

30%
20%
10%
0
-10%
-20%

Increase = 11% in areas studied

Donohue et al, GRL (June 2013) DOI: 10.1002/grl.50563

Fig. 18. Greening of the earth between 1982 and 2010 from the increase in CO₂. [Source: **Geophysical Research Letters**]

Fish and Coral Reefs: Typical crisis writings tell us all the barrier reefs will be gone in 50 years,[689] and that warmer waters will produce vast dead zones of dead fish, including shellfish, plankton, and coral.[690] But the problems related to the continued existence of fish are more closely related to excess fishing, as the UN reported in 2016 that about 90% of fish stocks are overfished.[691] [692] You already know that many coral reefs can do quite well at higher temperatures and low pH[693] and that they can thrive in parts of the Pacific Ocean where the pH is lowest and the water is warmest.

Animal Extinction: The Paris Agreement predicts that a one degree increase from current temperatures by 2100 will cause numerous extinctions,[694] and animals will become crammed and 18% of insects will become too crowded.[695 696 697] Why should these predictions be any better than those appearing in Al Gore's *An Inconvenient Truth,* which were all wrong? Where is the Climate Activist scholar who can identify any major animal extinctions?

Flooding and Hurricanes: The Paris Agreement supporters tell us that "Most rivers…will flood more often and the hotter atmosphere will produce more intense monsoons, violent storms, and extreme rainfall;"[698] and flooding will create 30 to 60 million refugees at a 1/2 degree increase from current temperatures. [699 700] But we know that during the past 50 years there has been no increase in flooding, hurricanes, or cyclones.[701 702 703]

It is interesting that the Climate Activists have been very quiet about hurricanes during 2021. Perhaps this is because 2021 had the fewest hurricanes since measurements were initially taken by satellite.

Figure 59: Number of Hurricanes 1980-2021 [704 705]

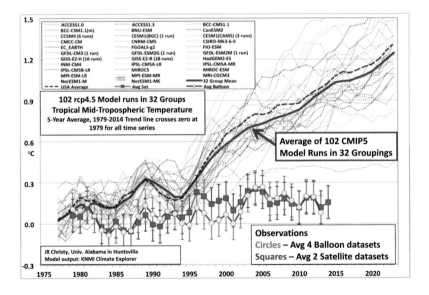

Conclusion: Since humanity started to use fossil fuels for energy, we have seen the greatest increase in wealth, health, education, and life span than at any time in world history. Meanwhile, almost every past catastrophic prediction by the Climate Activists has proved wrong. There is simply no historic justification for the predictions by the Paris Agreement supporters that another 1°C increase in temperature will cause humanity to be sicker, poorer, or more ignorant.

Biased News in the Social Media

In the first chapter, you read about the Oregon Petition which was signed by 30,000 scientists who believed that global warming was not a problem. They opposed the Kyoto Protocol of 1997 and most certainly would have voted against the Paris Agreement. A good example of biased news is the first citing on Google relating to the Oregon Petition, where Google claims it was a disinformation campaign.[704] On the other hand, the Google algorithms almost completely refuse to inform us of even one negative feature relating to the enormous expense and lack of value of the Paris Agreement. Instead, many of the Google citings inform us that the agreement is too weak and inadequate to prevent the destruction of our civilization.[705] Here is a typical citing. "The carbon emission goals are not nearly ambitious enough…. Climatologists have long said that just a 2-degree increase will cause a worldwide catastrophe. The participating countries need to significantly increase their individual carbon reduction efforts."[706] With such bias in the media, is it any surprise that millions of Americans support the Paris Agreement?

Chapter 7 Quiz

	True	False
1. CO_2 emissions fell substantially during the COVID-19 pandemic in 2020, causing global surface temperatures to decrease.	☐	☐
2. The number and intensity of hurricanes and forest fires decreased during the COVID-19 pandemic in 2020.	☐	☐
3. The Green New Deal is mainly about finding ways to reduce CO_2 emissions.	☐	☐
4. Enactment of the Green New Deal would substantially reduce CO_2 emissions and consequently lower future global surface temperatures.	☐	☐
5. The Paris Agreement addresses the need to prevent global surface temperatures from rising more than 1.5°C above the current temperature.	☐	☐
6. The Paris Agreement concludes that an increase in more than 2°C from current temperatures will be catastrophic.	☐	☐
7. The predictions being made by those who support the Paris Agreement are all consistent with past history and empirical scientific facts.	☐	☐
8. Predictions by the U.N. and the U.S. government regarding fish and animal extinctions, including polar bears, have proven to be accurate.	☐	☐
9. The IPCC, EPA, and NOAA have made accurate predictions of temperature increase, global warming, and climate change.	☐	☐
10. Al Gore correctly predicted that 16 animals, including certain geese, whales, and seals, would become extinct due to global warming.	☐	☐

The answers to all of the questions are False. Here's why:

1. Global average temperatures and atmospheric levels of CO_2 did not fall or stop rising during the COVID-19 pandemic in 2020, even though human-caused CO_2 emissions fell.

2. The number and intensity of hurricanes and forest fires did not diminish during the 2020 COVID-19 pandemic.

3. The Green New Deal includes trillions of dollars for social programs that have nothing to do with climate change.

4. If adopted, the Green New Deal would have virtually no effect on global warming or climate change, though it would massively increase the U.S. government debt.

5. Since current temperatures are already about 1°C higher than pre-Industrial Revolution levels, the Paris Agreement calls only for the future temperature rise to be kept to .5°C from current temperatures.

6. The Paris Agreement claimed there would be catastrophic results if temperatures increased by 1°C above current temperatures.

7. The predictions being made by supporters of the Paris Agreement, like those made by Climate Activists in the past, are contradicted by past history and empirical scientific facts.

8. The polar bears are thriving and there have been no meaningful extinctions of other fish or animals due to global warming or climate change.

9. Virtually all U.S. government and U.N. predictions have greatly missed their mark.

10. Al Gore has been 100% wrong in his predictions of animal extinctions.

FAKE NEWS: CODE RED! Around 2021, the European Commission, the group of European officials (bureaucrats) who review European tax policy, were addressing the carbon-tax (carbon dioxide tax) policy for airplanes. Their problem was that private aircraft, flown almost exclusively by the very wealthy and top government officials, used huge amounts of gasoline per person and the tax per private flyer would be very high. Obviously, the exceptionally rich and governments would prefer not paying such a tax. But how could the Commissioners develop a policy that would contribute to reducing temperature increases by 1/2°C without taxing all airplanes? Their creative decision was that ordinary passenger flights and cargo planes would be taxed, but private planes would be exempt from a carbon tax. Their justification did require creativity so they classified private aviation as primarily "business aviation," and, with equal leadership, compassion, and creativity, they decided that private flights for "pleasure" and "personal or recreational" purposes would also be tax exempt.

There were some people who thought that, since most of us use passenger planes and only the very rich use private travel, this policy should be reversed. My understanding is that, as of the time of this writing, the policy has not been finalized. Unfortunately, this is not **Fake News: Code Red.** Check it out.[707]

Summary

- **During the past 100 years, temperatures have increased one-degree Celcius and carbon dioxide has increased by over 100 ppm. During this time, poverty has diminished, and literacy, longevity, and wealth have increased.**

- **There is no validity to claims that, if temperatures and atmospheric carbon dioxide continue to increase as in the past, we will be poorer, more ignorant and have shorter lives as predicted by the Climate Activists.**

- **The decision to abide by the Paris Agreement and the Green New Deal will cost trillions of dollars. Implementation has been demanded by the U.N. IPCC and Climate Activists who have consistently made false predictions and recommendations in the past.**

Chapter 8
Activist Strategies

"We live at a time when emotions and feelings count more than truth, and there is a vast ignorance of science."
(James Lovelock, English scientist)

The author reveals the strategy behind the Activists' success in misleading millions of people to believe that global warming/climate change is the existential problem of our time and why their false, biased, and dangerous climate narrative should be ignored. These Activist strategies designed to confuse and mislead us include mischaracterizing consensus as science, using false and selective facts, bad assumptions, language distortion, hiding mistakes, controlling funding, scaring people, censorship, and intimidation. If you think of some others, please feel free to share them with the author.

―――――――――

Given that you are smart and have objectively reviewed what I have written, you understand that there is almost certainly no climate change "existential threat." So why are the Activists so effective in promoting their message, and why do so many people believe what they say? Here are some thoughts on the subject.

Mischaracterizing Consensus as Science

Real science systematically organizes knowledge in testable ways and proves conclusions decisively. Consensus, in contrast, is merely the appearance of agreement among a group of people. As you read earlier, Michael Crichton wrote, "There is no such thing as consensus science. If it is consensus, it is not science. If it is science, it is not consensus. Period!"[708] Earlier you have seen the global warming chart below, created by Professor Christy, University of Alabama, which reveals the consistently poor U.N. IPCC projections.

Figure 60: 102 Global Warming Projection Models with Flawed Consensus [709] [710]

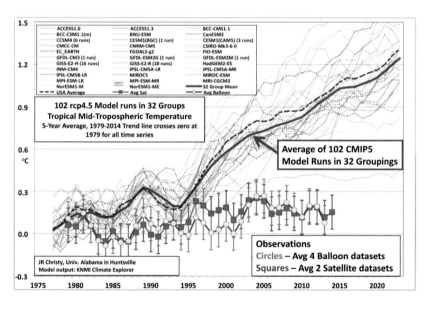

Although all of these models fail spectacularly and predict more warming than actually occurred, these are the models that the Climate Activists (the IPCC, EPA, NOAA, etc.) rely on to support their claim that global warming is a crisis. That's not "following the science." It's fraud.

It may be true that a majority of U.S. government experts, university professors, and journalists believe global warming is the greatest threat to our existence, but their hypothesis is simply wrong, and the data proves it. You have already seen scientific evidence, including:

- The Earth's temperature increased during the past 180 years by only 1°C.[711]

- During the past 5 years,[712] the Earth's temperature has not increased at all.

- Coral reefs faced with extreme "acidification" can outperform those growing in water with higher pH levels.[713] [714]

- The animal extinction predictions, including all of those in Al Gore's *An Inconvenient Truth,* have been wrong.

- There are more polar bears in the wild now than there were 50 years ago, thanks largely to laws preventing the shooting of polar bears. Climate change has nothing to do with their survival.[715]

My goal in writing this book was to give you enough ammunition so that you can help the Activists when they cite the "scientific consensus" argument that is contrary to science. As David Grimes wrote in *Good Thinking*, "Scientific claims don't derive their authority by virtue of coming from scientists. A scientific claim's acceptance stems from the weight of the evidence behind it".[716]

Using False and Selective Facts

According to legend, Casey Stengel, the famous New York Yankees baseball manager, was trying out a new center fielder who dropped several fly balls in a row. Stengel was disgusted, so he ran into center field to shag the fly balls himself and mentor his new center fielder. When the first ball was hit to Stengel, he put up his mitt to catch it, but dropped the ball. He threw his mitt to the ground and yelled at the new center fielder, "You got center field so screwed up that nobody can catch a ball now."

It may be that the constant barrage of false scientific information by the media, politicians, and vested interests has screwed up and confused Americans so that nobody will be able to effectively communicate the truth about climate change. The belief that climate change is a major problem in the United States is held by 90% of all Democrats, about 25% of

Republicans,[717] 57% of all Americans, and about 50% of the people in the world.[718] Thus, the majority of humanity believes that humans are causing serious climate damage and that governments should actively work to reduce the threat by limiting or ending the use of fossil fuels.

The use of false and selective facts is the backbone of the Activist propaganda campaign. Consider the following article headlines about forest fires:

- Climate change doubled the size of forest fires in Western U.S., study says[719]
- How climate change is increasing forest fires around the world[720]
- Global warming is the kindling that caused extensive wildfire[721]
- Wildfires and climate change: What's the connection?[722]
- How global warming has increased forest fires[723]
- There is a "strong connection between climate change and wildfires"[724] [725]

But we know from U.S. Government studies that the total number of fires has declined and that the great majority of forest fires are caused by arson, carelessness, utilities, and other human activities.[726] [727] Note the following scientific studies:

- Study shows 84 percent of wildfires caused by humans[728]
- What's the leading cause of wildfires in the U.S.? Humans[729]
- 90 percent of wildland fires caused by humans[730]
- Facts + statistics: Wildfires[731]
- People cause most U.S. wildfires[732]

If we don't know how many fires or exactly which fires are set by humans but we know that humans are causing most forest fires, shouldn't we concentrate on amending human behavior to address this issue? How can anybody honestly claim that global warming is exacerbating the forest fire problem? Only false and selective facts by the Activists could absolutely conclude that global warming causes more forest fires.

Figure 61: Global Temperatures vs. CO₂ [733]

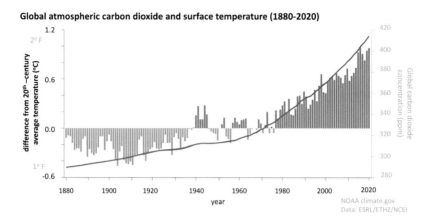

The U.S. Government (NOAA) chart above is an excellent example of presenting misleading statistics. Here are a few things to look at: (1) We know that since 1840 there has only been 2°F (1°C) increase in temperatures but the **BLACK** line extends 3°F (1.5C); (2) between 1944-1976, we know there was NO increase in temperature, but more than half of these years are pictured in **RED**; (3) The 5 years after 2017 are also pictured in **RED** even though temperatures have been lower since 2016. Shouldn't we expect the U.S. Government to be more objective?

Here is another chart printed in 2021 by the U.S. Government, which ends in 2017. What happened to 2018, 2019, and 2020? Do you think that the Government does not know that these years were cooler than 2016?

Figure 62: Yearly Surface Temperatures since 1950 [734]

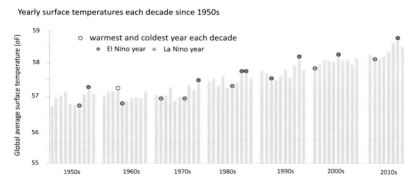

Bad Assumptions

It is a most excellent strategy for Activists to rely on computer models to lend credibility to their predictions because real-world data won't support their claims. Their computer models operate as "black boxes" that hide bad assumptions, faulty data, and even fraud. Why should anyone believe that computer projections are better than empirical data for making climate predictions? The chart at the beginning of this chapter proves there were major errors in 100 models relied on by the Climate Activists to make their predictions. Similar bad assumptions are behind claims that global warming is causing more hurricanes, droughts or flooding, and animal extinctions.

Climate Activists should have listened to Thucydides, the Greek historian and writer of *History of the Peloponnesian War,* when he wrote: "We study the past as a key to the future." Don't you think you should place your bets that sea levels will rise 1 inch every 8 years, as they have for 100 years, rather than U.N. predictions that sea levels will rise at four times that rate by 2100? Why should any rational person think there will be millions of sea-level refugees when there are none now? The next time you are confronted by an Activist, ask why the Activist computer projections almost always exceed reality. Could it be that their computer assumptions are in error?

Language Distortion

We saw earlier that Climate Activists call those who disagree with them "climate deniers" or "science deniers" even though they acknowledge that there is climate change and some global warming. Changing the meaning of words to limit or control debates has become an important weapon of the Activists.

An example of language distortion was the labeling of CO_2 as a "pollutant," a misnomer confirmed in a 5 to 4 decision by the U.S. Supreme Court in 2007. This decision was based on a claim that CO_2 somehow "disrupts the environment," [735] a false claim that enabled the EPA to regulate automobile gas mileage requirements. We are fortunate that the EPA did not ask the Supreme Court about water vapor since, by the same criteria, water vapor would have been labeled a pollutant even though it is essential to life. Besides, without CO_2 we probably would all be dead because all animals have a symbiotic relationship with plants, which need CO_2.[736] The Activists also trash the English language by claiming that water vapor is a *good and innocent* greenhouse gas that only does *bad* things because of CO_2.

In further defense of CO_2, observe that when we exhale CO_2, plants absorb the gas and store it as food energy; that CO_2 effectively extinguishes fire because it is heavier than air and spreads into a blanket that smothers the fire; and that the EPA has determined that CO_2 is safe even at 10 times its current air concentration. There is no scientific basis to conclude that CO_2 is a pollutant, but government bureaucrats have their own agenda, separate from science, and the Supreme Court, a group of attorneys that ignored the scientific facts, simply rubber-stamped the Activists' recommendation.

We should also consider the Activist distortion of the meaning of "significance," a word that has a specific meaning in statistics. This is a word the Activists intentionally misuse to claim scientific support for their positions, where none exists. For example, the increase in over 100 parts per million of atmospheric CO_2 can be "statistically significant" since it is a 25% increase since 1960. But this "statistically significant" increase in CO_2 has not created any "statistically significant" world-wide temperature increase, which is what Activists scream about.

My suggestion is that if someone tells you how seriously CO_2 is polluting the air, ask if the CO_2 we exhale with every breath is also "pollution" and if the increase in CO_2 as a greenhouse gas is so harmful, why water vapor, which is 20 times more abundant greenhouse gas is not harmful.

Hiding Mistakes

Climate Activists rarely, if ever, acknowledge their mistakes even though so many of their facts and projections of future temperatures, sea-level rise, hurricanes and floods, polar bears, and other animal extinctions are so often wrong. A specific example of denying an error is that even after Michael Mann's hockey stick temperature increase predictions have been proven wrong, the error was not acknowledged. Why should that be? Why can't the Activists admit when they erred?

One reason mistakes are hidden or denied is that the Activists can get away with it. The media will not report the correction; academic's colleagues will not expose the error for fear that they, too, will then be exposed and government grants will continue to flow only to researchers who support the original mistake. So, there are no negative consequences to promoting erroneous Activist claims.

Most importantly, admitting a single mistake can cause the whole false narrative of global warming to unravel. Science works that way: A false finding contradicts other findings, which, in turn, contradicts others and so on. If your theory predicts that animals, including polar bears, are going extinct, you must refute study after study based on real-world data showing that polar bears started flourishing immediately after shooting them became illegal. When the Activists predict once again that we have only 12 years left before the climate catastrophe, they will have to contend with the Babylon Bee's prediction that the Activists have only 12 years to change their prediction that we only have 12 more years before a climate catastrophe. The scientific method rejects falsehoods the way a healthy body rejects the flu. Mistakes in the climate debate remain hidden because Activists cannot afford to be wrong, not even once. The next time you are told to worry about climate change, consider asking them why they believe in Activist flooding when some of our major coastal cities, like Los Angeles, have experienced a total sea-level rise of less than 6 inches during the last 100 years. Bet they did not know that.

Bias

When scientists perform experiments that follow the scientific method and discover that reality differs from their beliefs, they change their minds. They abandon their original hypotheses and conduct new experiments to see if their new hypotheses match nature. This is how real science works. But biases prevent Climate Activists from doing this because they become passionate about climate change, so they don't bother to understand reality.

When data contradicts their theses, like in Palau where coral reefs flourish in warm and less basic water or when global temperatures increase and sea-level rises are minimal, Activists seek or invent new data that appears to support their original hypotheses and then use their influence to support their bias. A typical example of bias with no scientific confirmation is the claim that climate change is a significant threat to our national security,[737] a claim that Homeland Security, the Defense Department, and the National Security Agency all confirm. Isn't it clear that there must be significant bias for anyone even to propose climate change as a national security issue? Doesn't this appear to be nonsense?

As David Grimes wrote in *Good Thinking,* "The onus (the burden of proof) is always on those making the claim to support it rather than for others to disprove it. Attempts to shift the burden of proof are a warning sign of bad science."[738] Activist climate science, corrupted by bias, has become pure advocacy and propaganda and should not be considered science. One reason Climate Activists at universities either say nothing about false data or repeat untruths so often is because their incomes, careers, and reputations depend on supporting the climate disaster narrative.

The next time you see your Atmospheric Science professor, ask him if he could keep his job if he wrote a paper that proved that the major human causes of coral reef bleaching have nothing to do with climate change and everything to do with the 6,000 tons of human sunscreens deposited yearly or the garbage, refuse, agricultural runoff, or copper from marine paints.

Controlling Government Funding

Currently, worldwide about $630 billion is spent to "fight climate change,"[739] and about $3 billion is spent by the U.S. government for research on Oceanic and Atmospheric Science. U.S. government decision makers and university professors march in lockstep to make sure that all funding goes to Activists or those who support Activist beliefs. I have been unable to locate even one grant to a Realist scientist.[740]

Suppose you were a university scientist and wanted to do a study to evaluate the Paris Agreement claim that a 2°C temperature increase would destroy the Earth. You point out that your thesis is that if CO_2 increases as in the past, plants and trees will likely thrive; more animals will not become extinct; human literacy rate and life expectancies and financial wealth will all increase. A study of this nature would confirm that the Paris Agreement is meaningless and is leading us toward a terrible waste of resources. What do you think your chances would be to get U.S. government funding? The correct answer is "Zero." This is because virtually all research grants for climate change go to the Activists.[741] To receive federal funds, it is mandatory that a professor's position be that man-made global warming is an existential threat requiring major social and economic change.[742]

Since most universities depend heavily on government grants to fund research, any hope of becoming a tenured professor in environmental studies at any major liberal arts university requires that you seek government grants using the proper opinion. The fact is that nearly all Government research grants must defend the existential threat hypothesis, which makes invisible any objective research on climate change. This one-sided Activist climate change funding monopoly provides justification to doubt Government-sponsored research. Why should we believe any of it?

To find independently funded scientific research, investigate a non-profit think tank such as the American Enterprise Institute, Competitive Enterprise Institute, Heartland Institute, or the Heritage Foundation. These experts provide scientific climate knowledge without the bias demanded by those who must chase government grants to keep their faculty positions.

Scaring People

Climate Activists have assigned to the media the delicate job of scaring people. For example, the *Guardian* reports, "Drowned cities; stagnant seas; intolerable heatwaves; entire nations uninhabitable. A four-degree-warmer world is the stuff of nightmares and yet that's where we're heading in just decades."[743] Let's acknowledge that it takes a great deal of skill to write anything so scary. It also takes great "chutzpah"[744] to write anything that fictitious. There is nothing in the *Guardian* prediction that is consistent with previous empirical experience.

As you know, it would be very scary to lose all our polar bears and have thousands of animals become extinct. Let's look at a few Activist warnings:

- Global Warming is Driving Polar Bears Toward Extinction, Researchers Say[745]
- Commentary: Arctic Habitat Needs to be Saved for Polar Bears[746]
- Polar Bears Could Face Extinction By 2100 Due to Climate Change, Study Says[747]
- Almost 30,000 Species Face Extinction Because of Human Activity[748]
- Nearly All Coral Reefs Will Disappear Over the Next 20 years[749]

At some deep level, we all want to be scared: it triggers our "fight or flight" reflex and imagination, bringing some excitement to our day. Activists know this, so they inundate us with headlines, news, and stories designed to make us afraid, very afraid. These are false warnings based on shoddy science. Don't allow this to happen to you. Instead, consider feeling sorry for the writer's ignorance. Isn't it sad that the author might believe the false impending disasters when he writes this junk? Just think about how unhappy the author must be if he believes that the polar bears and 30,000 other species will become extinct!

Censorship

One strategy the Climate Activists use to confuse and mislead us is to make invisible all facts that contradict their beliefs. Colleges and universities rarely invite Climate Realists to speak on campus, and when they do, protesters are often allowed to disrupt their talks. Publications simply refuse to print articles by Climate Realists. Just think about how NASA could easily publish an article titled "How Climate Change May Be Impacting Storms over Earth's Tropical Oceans."[750] Now, just think about any entity publishing an article titled "How Climate Change May *Not* Be Impacting Storms over Earth's Tropical Oceans." You have seen the scientific facts that we have had many years, like 2021, with very modest hurricane activity.

But where in the main media can you find this example of no meaningful climate change? If it is ever mentioned, it will be called "an anomaly" (something unusual).

Social media and search engines have been especially thorough in censoring Realists by using "fact-check" posts, putting Realists in "Social Media Jail," or posting negative disclaimers when Realists share the truth. Google is perhaps the master of censorship. For example, Google makes the fact that between 2006 and 2015, there were no major hurricanes hard to locate and almost invisible. [751] If you look up this issue, Google will most likely provide you with multiple citings of misleading information relating to the increased intensity of hurricanes.[752] You will have to search until about the seventh page to find out that the actual intensification is less than 3%.[753] Almost nowhere is the information that you were seeking that would confirm the quiet hurricane activity between 2006 and 2015. This is typical of how Google's algorithms favor the Activist narrative.

The censorship by the Activists reveals the weakness of their positions. After all, if you have strong arguments, there is no need for censorship. Realists generally welcome discussion and debate because their positions are usually strongly supported by science. Where can you obtain Realist information?

Try these sites:

- CFACT.org
- Climate Change Weekly
- Climatedepot.com
- Junkscience.com
- Nongovernmental International Panel on Climate Change
- The Heartland Institute
- The CO_2 Coalition
- The Competitive Enterprise Institute
- Wattsupwiththat.com

Intimidation

Finally, Activists often resort to intimidation. Some Climate Realists report receiving expletive-laden emails and letters, threats of physical violence, and even death threats. Some have been threatened with losing, and some lose their academic positions. Donors to organizations that allow the Climate Realist position to be expressed have been targeted by Activist groups with letter and email campaigns, boycotts, shareholder petitions, and "disinvestment" campaigns.

If the climate change debate were just a debate about science and economics, such tactics would be unnecessary and denounced by both sides. But in the climate debate, they are common and overwhelmingly come from the Activist side.[754]

In 2019, my wife and I supported a debate on global warming at our alma mater.[755] We were told that there would be no debate notices allowed. The debate was to be kept secret from all who were not members of the debate class because students would likely march or interrupt and force its termination. Apparently, this is because global warming is considered "settled science" on campus, and any unrestricted debate on it could "trigger" some students and faculty members.

A recent survey found 62% of all Americans are afraid to express their views on anything political.[756] The intimidation doesn't go both ways equally; about 50% of self-described liberals are reluctant to express their views, but 77% of conservatives, who would be more likely to oppose the common global warming narrative, report being intimidated.[757]

Regardless of where you fall on the spectrum between "Activist" and "Realist," you should agree that intimidation is never appropriate and should be condemned in the strongest language. If the debate over climate change remains stifled, then our chances of doing what is best for our country will continue to be in jeopardy.

Chapter 8 Quiz

	True	False
1. **Consensus:** Activists prove that Consensus is the same as science.	☐	☐
2. **Using Scientific Facts:** Activists provide accurate and complete information.	☐	☐
3. **Objective Assumptions:** Activists use computer projections that have valid hypotheses.	☐	☐
4. **Proper Language Use:** Activists use standard English in traditional ways so that their messages are clear.	☐	☐
5. **Admitting Mistakes:** Activists disclose any errors they make immediately.	☐	☐
6. **Objectivity:** Activists' conclusions carefully avoid Confirmation Bias.	☐	☐
7. **Balanced Funding**: Activists are careful to award grants based on merit and ignore political considerations..	☐	☐
8. **Provide us with Confidence**: Activists never warn us of catastrophes if their ideas are not followed.	☐	☐
9. **Open Minded:** Activists support multiple ideas to reach the public.	☐	☐
10. **Welcome Dissenters**: Activists always treat those with whom they disagree with warmth and respect.	☐	☐

All of the answers to the Quiz are False. Here's why:

1. **Mischaracterizing Consensus:** Activists pretend that Consensus is the same as science.

2. **Using False and Selective Facts:** Activists provide misleading and incomplete information.

3. **Bad Assumptions:** Activists use biased computer projections that ignore history.

4. **Language Distortion**: Activists misuse the English language.

5. **Hiding Mistakes:** Activists ignore past projections which have been wrong.

6. **Bias**: Activists' conclusions are based on Confirmation Bias.

7. **Controlling Funding**: Activists guide monies only to those with whom they agree.

8. **Scaring People:** Activists threaten humanity with catastrophe if their ideas are not followed.

9. **Censorship**: Activists prevent opposing ideas from reaching the public.

10. **Intimidation:** Activists attack opponents with lawsuits and verbal assaults.

FAKE NEWS: CODE RED! Today, in the U.S. and throughout the world, there is a war between the Activists and the Realists. It is a war for our minds, our emotions, and our pocketbooks.

To address this issue, I want to compare competing ideas. I want to share with you the thoughts of a world-class leading Activist, John Cook, who writes the Skeptical Science blog and is the author of a cartoon book for children called *Crazy Uncle vs. Climate Change.*[758]

As you know, the Earth has increased in temperature by about 1°C during the past 100 years and fossil fuels generate atmospheric CO_2 which is slowly heating the atmosphere. This is believed by both Realists and Activists. But Cook tells us in *Crazy Uncle* that Realists (whom he pejoratively calls Climate Deniers) believe the recent rise in CO_2 is all natural;[759] that Realists believe we are heading into an ice age[760] [761] and that global warming stopped in 1998. I have never met a Climate Realist scientist who believes any of this. I wonder, what is Cook's source for these statements?

His book states that CO_2 is a "hard core pollutant"[762] and that human-caused global warming threatens the survival of polar bears (even though he admits there are more polar bears now than 50 years ago.)[763] But we know that plants need CO_2 to survive and that we need plants to survive. Besides, the EPA has determined that CO_2 is not toxic at 10 times its current concentration. I don't blame Cook for claiming global warming could prevent the survival of the polar bears because Activists need the soft and cuddly looking polar bear to support their fund-raising efforts.

Cook criticizes the Realists for not believing that sea levels have accelerated and for believing that oceans have risen at almost a constant rate for 120 years. [764] Does he know, for example, the Los Angeles sea levels have risen fewer than 6 inches during the last century? How worried should we be about that?[765]

Cook does not mention that there has been no global warming since 2016, even though his book was written in 2020. Why not? How can he be certain that temperatures will increase in the future when they haven't for the past 5 years? Perhaps Cook is disappointed that nature has not cooperated to produce a warmer climate recently.

Why does Cook frighten the children reading his book by writing that the increase in atmospheric CO_2 is generating the energy of 4 atomic bombs per second? Cook certainly knows about NASA telling us that "Every 1.5 millionth of a second, the sun releases more energy than all humans consume in an entire year."[766] A meaningful portion of this energy is directed to Earth, and thus the sun provides us with thousands of times more energy than human-caused fossil fuel emissions.[767]

Perhaps you recall the messages at the top of two of the preceding chapters: "We are being hit with a massive wave of misinformation about climate change" and "In order to counter misinformation, we need to understand the impact it has. The most obvious is causing us to believe things that aren't true."

These were quotes from *Crazy Uncle*, but they seem to apply to Cook's bias and questionable science. So, who is telling the truth about this existential crisis? The Realists or the Activists? Which group is feeding you the **FAKE NEWS: CODE RED?**

Summary

- The Climate Activist strategies, which are supported by most universities, government agencies, and social media, are based on false and selective facts, censorship of opposing ideas, intimidation, false scares, controlling of environmental funding, bias, hiding mistakes, bad assumptions and falsely claiming that consensus is science.

Chapter 9

Greta

*The author encourages the reader to not be bullied by Greta
and the other Activists and to ignore their claims about
mass extinction of animals and their demands we meet some
arbitrary CO_2 limitation; that the readers recognize that
these Activist claims are mostly that of a religious cult and
there is no reason for us to feel uncomfortable, unhappy,
or scared.*

*Their alarms deserve none of our time, efforts, or money;
their focus on trying to modify our climate is senseless,
harmful, expensive, and impossible. Any Activist
implementation will only make us poorer. We should
stop them from implementing their destructive ideas and
concentrate on embracing things of value, helping others, and
generating happiness.*

Greta Thunberg

Greta Thunberg is the world's most effective Climate Activist. Born in 2003, Greta calls herself a "climate activist." Of significance are her passion, her aggressive word choice, and her brilliant ability to communicate. Her delivery is powerful, emotional, and heartfelt. She scolds us and attacks us for what she claims is our complacency.

Greta has spoken in front of the U.N. General Assembly, U.S. Congress, European Parliament, French National Assembly, and British Parliament. She has been honored as a Time Magazine Person of the Year, awarded many prizes, and has more than 2.5 million followers on Facebook. Her speeches are almost always followed by standing ovations. Greta gives speeches like those given by other Activists: she just expresses their thoughts more effectively.

Greta has many criticisms of everyone. Here are her thoughts on our failure to address global warming and how this has adversely affected her. [768]

Greta Says:

- "Treat the Climate Activist like the acute crisis it is and give us a future. Our lives are in your hands."[769]
- "We can't save the world by playing by the rules…So everyone out there: it is now time for civil disobedience. It is time to rebel."[770]
- "I care about climate justice and the living planet."[771]
- "How dare you continue to look away and come here saying that you are doing enough."[772]
- "Your generation is failing us…. And if you choose to fail us, I say we will never forgive you."[773]

I believe Greta Thunberg is a fine person. This chapter is not intended to attack her personally in any way. My criticisms relate to her unsupportable scientific claims and her policy recommendations which are impractical, economically false, based on ignorance, and improperly attack us.

The Sixth Mass Extinction

Greta says:

- "People are suffering, people are dying. We are in the middle of a mass extinction."[774]
- "We are in the midst of the Sixth Mass Extinction, with about 200 species going extinct every single day."[775]

Quite possibly, you are unfamiliar with the various past mass extinctions. As a refresher, here is a summary for your review.[776] Since all these extinctions occurred over 50 million years ago and none of us were around to observe them, much of this information is based on interpretations of fossil records.

First Mass Extinction: 440 million (or possibly 540 million) years ago, very small marine organisms became extinct when they were destroyed by multi-celled animals.[777] Some scientists believe it was caused by a sustained decrease in the level of oxygen in the ocean.[778]

Second Mass Extinction: 365 million years ago, many tropical marine species became extinct because there were large increases in poisonous lead and arsenic in the oceans.[779]

Third Mass Extinction: 250 million years ago, the largest mass extinction in Earth's history destroyed many vertebrates and fish. The air warmed by about 10°C, which made breathing difficult for animals. The oceans heated up, which reduced the available oxygen, and multiple metals and sulfides polluted the oceans and killed many fish.[780]

Fourth Mass Extinction: 210 million years ago, there was intense volcanic activity. Volcanoes, mostly in Siberia and the Atlantic Ocean, emitted ash, soot, and gases that killed many land vertebrates. Volcanic activity blotted out the sun; the oceans became acidic; the air and water lost significant oxygen. Day after day, for millions of years, this continued until there was almost no life on Earth. Some reports of the Fourth Mass Extinction claim volcanoes spewed out gases, including sulfur dioxide, hydrogen sulfide, hydrochloric acid, carbon monoxide and, of course, carbon dioxide and water vapor.

The volcanoes also spewed out solid particles, including fragments of rocks, minerals, and volcanic glass,[781] [782] which ranged from fine and gritty particles the size of a grain of rice or as cinders ranging from a fraction of an inch to 2.5 inches.[783]

It was after the Fourth Mass Extinction that the dinosaurs flourished. It is believed that their successful growth was due to their upright stance, which allowed them to move more quickly than their predecessors and their warm-blood which enabled them to survive because it reduced their reliance on the sun to warm their bodies.[784] Their warm-blood required air that was much richer in oxygen than we have today.[785] [786] Initially, all the land masses existed within one continent, referred to as Pangea. When the continents split up, the dinosaurs became separated.

Fifth Mass Extinction: This occurred about 65 million years ago and was caused by an asteroid that killed not only the dinosaurs but also half of the remaining animals and plants.[787]

This brings us to Greta and her claims of a *Sixth Mass Extinction*. The most cited article on the subject was published in *Science* in 2015 by Geraldo Ceballos and Paul Ehrlich with the title *"Accelerated Modern Human-induced Species Losses: Entering the Sixth Mass Extinction."* [788] The article states, "The evidence is incontrovertible that recent extinction rates are unprecedented in human history and highly unusual in Earth's history. Our analysis emphasizes that our global society has started to destroy species of other organisms at an accelerating rate, initiating a mass extinction episode unparalleled for 65 million years."

Doesn't it make you feel terrible when Greta and the Activists inform you that we are amid the *Sixth Mass Extinction*? Don't you wonder which of the beautiful animals you see at the zoo or which of the beautiful flowers you have in your home will disappear? Greta terrorizes us with the claim that up to 200 species become extinct every day due to global warming.

This means that more than 50,000 plant and animal species that will disappear this year!

Fortunately, *Yale Environment 360* did a study which concluded that there is no *Sixth Mass Extinction* with 200 species disappearing each day. According to their report, these claims are "based on computer modeling, and documented losses are tiny by comparison. Only about 800 extinctions have been documented in the past 400 years. Out of some 1.9 million recorded current or recent species on the planet, that represents less than a tenth of one percent."[789] [790]

Rainforest ecologist Nigel Stork wrote, "There are almost no empirical data to support estimates of current extinctions of 100, or even one species a day."[791] There is no problem here. So, we can stop worrying!

Ask yourself or your friends if they can identify even one animal that has disappeared this year during the "Sixth Mass Extinction." If you are looking for claimed verification that many animals are headed toward extinction, you will likely find that *Earth.org is* a major supporter of this theory. The warning by *Earth.org* includes, "The land vertebrates on the brink of extinction include the Sumatran Rhino, the Española Giant Tortoise (*a.k.a.* the Galapagos Tortoise, a large turtle) and the Harlequin Frog."[792] [793] Here is a short summary of what really happened to these rhinos, turtles, and frogs: The rhinos and turtles were shot or eaten, and the frogs died of a fungus infection. Global warming was not involved. Here are some details:

Figure 63: Sumatran Rhino [794]

Sumatran Rhino: Personally, I don't care for rhinos because they are dangerous, frightening, and unattractive. However, the thought of rhinos disappearing from the Earth due to global warming because of our selfish use of fossil fuels strikes me as an unacceptable loss.

The good news is the Sumatran Rhino is not extinct, and that fossil fuels are not harming them. Unfortunately, it is true that humans have almost caused the extinction of the Sumatran Rhino by shooting them in trophy hunting and using their horns as aphrodisiacs or folk medicines that cure fevers or infections, and carving their horns into necklaces, bracelets, or beads.[795]

As reported by the Rhino Organization, "Because of poaching, numbers have decreased by more than 70% over the last 20 years with the only viable populations in Indonesia."[796] Sumatran rhinos are "physically guarded by Rhino Protection Units" in secured areas.[797] Clearly, the 1°C temperature increase on Earth during the past 100 years had less to do with the rhinos' potential extinction than bullets! Clearly any rhino that is thinking straight would agree that climate change has nothing to do with the possible Sixth Mass Extinction and are much more concerned about being shot to death. If you have an interest in supporting the Sumatran Rhino, consider a donation to savetherhino.org.

Figure 64: Galapagos Tortoise[798]

Galapagos Tortoise is another animal claimed to be heading toward extinction because of global warming. The Galapagos Tortoise is unique: It is the largest of all turtles, often lives for more than 100 years, and can weigh more than 400 pounds.[799] Their numbers declined from over 250,000 in the

17th century to a low of around 3,000 in the 1970s, and today about 15,000 are alive in the wild.[800]

In the seventeenth century, pirates and shippers would capture the tortoises and store them in the ship's hold until their succulent meat and high-quality oil were needed. The tortoises had no natural predators until humans introduced animals hostile to tortoises (rats, goats, and pigs).[801]

I have not been able to find anything in the literature which would indicate that the Galapagos tortoise is endangered because of global warming. If you have an interest in supporting the Galapagos Tortoise, consider a donation to WWF (worldwildlife.org).

Figure 65: Harlequin Frog [802]

The *Harlequin Frog* is another example claimed by Activists to be a species headed for extinction due to global warming. Harlequin Frogs come in many different colors, often a black skin covered with a stripe or dots. It turns out that the same fungi, the Chytrid[803] that attacked the Costa Rican Golden Toads caused the fatal skin infection that destroyed the Harlequin Frog in Panama. [804] [805]

Temperatures did not increase during the time of Harlequin Frogs' distress, so Activists switched their claims and blamed fossil fuels for "climate fluctuations," which endangered the frogs. Although some ecologists such as Alan Pounds of the Tropical Science Center claim "warming temperatures have single-handedly triggered the spread of the fungus,"[806] there seems to be little scientific support for this claim, especially since the infections are worse in the winter.[807] [808] [809] Besides, since the Chytrid does not thrive at temperatures over 23°C,[810] it is unreasonable to blame global warming for a fungus that does not like warm temperatures. If you have an interest in supporting the Harlequin Frog, consider a donation to Global Wildlife Conservation.

Summary: If we stop shooting the rhinos, eating the turtles, and do a better job protecting the frogs from the Chytrid fungus, all three of these species could live in peace.

The Carbon Budget

Greta says:

- "People are not aware that there is a carbon budget and just how small the remaining carbon budget is."[811]
- Exceeding the carbon budget will cause "irreversible chain reactions beyond human control."[812]
- "Around the year 2030 … we will set off an irreversible chain reaction beyond our control that will most likely lead to the end of our civilization as we know it."[813]
- "Now we have less than 340 gigatons of CO_2 left to emit in that budget to share fairly."[814]

Greta and the other Activists tell us that there will be a catastrophe once atmospheric CO_2 reaches a certain level. The Carbon Budget is a fixed amount of what the Activists claim is an allowable amount of atmospheric CO_2. So where did this idea originate? One early reference came in 2008 from a report by the German Advisory Council on Global Change (WBGU)[815] which claimed humans could release into the atmosphere only a certain amount of CO_2, and no more, without causing a climate catastrophe. Greta has stated numerous times that exceeding this Carbon Budget would be a Tipping Point resulting in an Irreversible Chain Reaction and Catastrophic climate change.

A gigaton (GT) is one billion tons. According to the climate budget theory, if we put 1,900 GT of CO_2 into the atmosphere by 2050, temperatures will rise 2°C more than in pre-Industrial times (1°C more than current temperatures) and exceed the maximum temperature increase dictated by the Paris Agreement.

As of January 2020, humans have caused about 1,600 GT of CO_2 since the beginning of the Industrial Revolution and have only about 300 GT left before we will cause the Earth's devastation.[816] [817] In other words, we have used up more than 80% of our carbon budget. Greta tells us we are releasing about 40 GT of CO_2 per year,[818] which will cause us to exceed our climate budget prior to 2030. She warns us that as a result of our selfishness and complacency, "Millions of people worldwide are in for a disastrous future of hunger, drought, and disease."[819] Furthermore, she informs us that "A number of leading climate scientists" have confirmed that it is already too late to head off this "nightmare scenario."[820]

Isn't that frightening?

The source for many of Greta's claims is the U.N. IPCC which proclaimed, in 2019, that we had only 11 years (until 2030) to prevent "irreversible damage from climate change."[821] According to María Garcés, president of the U.N.'s General Assembly in 2019, "we are the last generation that can prevent irreparable damage to our planet."[822]

Since we have used up 80% of our Carbon Budget, shouldn't there be some evidence anywhere that there will be an "Irreversible Chain Reaction beyond our control that will most likely lead to the end of our civilization as we know it."[823] Greta has warned and threatened us of its inevitability!

We know that there has been no great acceleration in sea-level rise;[824] no increase in major storms, fires, flooding, or droughts;[825] and no losses of polar bears or evidence of significant animal extinctions[826] due to global warming. Do you think that re-education might help Greta?

Other Famous Climate Change Predictions

Greta is only one of many Activists who have threatened us with warnings of global warming disasters. And every previous "tipping point" prediction by past Activists has been proven false. Note the following examples:[827] [828] [829]

- 1989: U.N. claimed we had 10 years left. … "entire nations wiped off the Earth if global warming is not reversed by 2000." (Noel Brown)
- 2009: "Only 50 days left to save the world from global warming." (British Prime Minister Gordon Brown)
- 2009: "Only 96 months left" to save the planet from "irretrievable climate and ecosystem collapse." (Prince Charles)
- 2009: If no action before 2012, it will be "too late." (Rajendra Pachauri, former head of IPCC)
- 2012: This is "the last window of opportunity." (Tim Wirth, President, U.N. Foundation)
- 2014: "Only 500 days to stop climate chaos." (Laurent Fabius, French Foreign Minister)
- 2015: This is the "last effective opportunity" to stop catastrophic warming. (World leaders at the Vatican)[830]

Settled Science

Greta says:

- "There is no room for discussion: The Climate Crisis has already been solved. We already have all the facts and solutions. All we must do is to wake up and change."[831]
- "If emissions have to stop, then we must stop the emissions. To me that is black or white."[832]
- "There are no gray areas when it comes to survival. Either we go on as a civilization or we don't."[833]

Based on the empirical history of the Earth and all the scientific evidence presented in the preceding chapters, Greta is completely wrong about all these statements. The debate is far from settled. Many of us believe that based on science, reducing CO_2 emissions is not necessary or desirable.[834] There is no evidence that, to date, global warming is an existential threat.

Summary of Scientific Facts

Here are some of the scientific facts presented earlier in this book that confirm Greta's ignorance:

- Atmospheric CO_2 levels have slowly and steadily increased since the start of the Industrial Revolution. Today they are about 100 ppm higher than 50 years ago.
- Average global surface temperature has risen about 1°C since 1840, *but not in pace with CO_2 levels.*
- The warming trend began long before man-made CO_2 could have been a factor, and temperature rise has been unsteady, interrupted by long pauses.
- Global sea level has been rising at a slow and steady rate since the end of the last Ice Age. There is no sign that the rate of sea-level rise is rapidly accelerating due to man-made global warming.
- Hurricanes, tornadoes, and cyclones are no more frequent and no more intense than they were 50 years ago.
- The COVID-19 pandemic, which generated the largest single reduction in fossil fuel use in our lifetime, had no measurable effect on temperature, climate, or sea levels.

- Global warming should not get blamed for forest fires, which are primarily caused by carelessness, arson, utilities, and other human-controlled activities.

- Polar bears are not headed toward extinction. In fact, they are flourishing since hunting became severely restricted.

- No major animals have gone extinct during the past 50 years due to global warming.

- Many, many coral reefs are thriving in locations around the world with relatively warm seawater and low pH levels ("acidified").

Greta's statement that we have "all of the facts and all of the solutions" is contrary to reality and is total scientific nonsense. Reality is that many of her "facts" are imaginary and her "solutions" are unnecessary. They would destroy rather than help protect human civilization and the natural world.

Money

Greta says:

- "And all you can talk about is money and fairy tales of eternal economic growth. How dare you!" [835]

- "We are about to sacrifice our civilization for the opportunity of a very small number of people to continue to make enormous amounts of money."[836]

- "We are about to sacrifice the biosphere so that rich people in countries like mine can live in luxury."[837]

As you know, there is graft, theft, and numerous other illegal ways to make money and become rich, but the vast majority of wealthy people worked hard, had original ideas, and provided value to other people. There is no truth to the claim that greedy people are the cause of global warming.

Greta, who became a millionaire before she turned 18 years old,[838] is already among the wealthiest 1%. How did she become a millionaire? By giving speeches that frightened millions of people. You have read what her messages are: That we are amid a mass extinction that is causing the deaths of thousands of animals! That we are exceeding a mythical Carbon

Budget that will cause "Irreversible Chain Reactions," which will make the Earth almost uninhabitable!

For no legitimate reason or justification, based on highly questionable or outright false "scientific facts," she is scaring millions of children and adults with her speeches. I have not been able to find any mention of the cost of the environmental policies she demands. The American Action Forum estimates the Green New Deal would cost $51 trillion to $93 trillion over 10 years. The program's own authors admit it would cost at least $10 trillion.[839]

Where would the money come from? Greta says it should come from rich people with "money and fairy tales of eternal economic growth." But reducing CO_2 emissions requires making energy more expensive, and every study of the matter concludes that higher energy prices hurt the poor more than the rich.[840] Greta would take money away from middle- and low-income people who have earned their money and give it to wealthy and politically connected elites who make their money by financing environmentally questionable renewable energy and receive tax credits and subsidies for electric cars and ethanol. Greta never mentions that 99% of us who use electricity and fossil fuels are poorer than she and would be hurt by the policies she recommends.

Religion and Climate

Greta says:

- "I don't want your hope. I don't want you to be hopeful. I want you to panic. I want you to feel the fear I feel every day… and then I want you to act."[841]

- "Your generation is failing us. But the young people are starting to understand your betrayal."[842]

- "The eyes of all future generations are upon you and if you choose to fail us, I say we will never forgive you."[843]

If you believe something without any facts or historical empirical science for support, then the basis of your beliefs must be faith. Faith-based beliefs are religious beliefs, and there is a strong religious tone to Greta's claims.

Naturally this brings me to Jonathan Edwards.[844] In the early eighteenth-century, Jonathan Edwards was America's most prominent theologian. The most famous sermon he preached was titled *Sinners in the Hands of an Angry God*. In this sermon, he stated that the Wicked deserve to be taken to Hell and that divine justice does not prevent God from destroying the Wicked at any moment. Therefore, the Wicked should feel insecure. To eliminate this Wickedness, all they had to do to save themselves from Hell was to accept God.[845] [846] Bryan Jackson at the University of Arizona commented that "Edwards used descriptions of the reality of Hell to invoke psychosomatic reactions of terror in his audience."[847]

Jonathan Edwards

The similarities between the messages of Jonathan Edwards and Greta Thunberg are clear. Both have told us we are wicked, and we are either going to Hell or creating a Hell on Earth. Greta's message is even more extreme than Edwards' because to go to Hell for Edwards was an individual matter and only the guilty would go to Hell. Also, Hell to Edwards could come only after you died. To Greta, not only are you, as an individual, going to Hell, but you are bringing everyone else with you. You are personally guilty, not only of destroying yourself, but of mass destruction of the Earth and all humanity.

Greta is accusing us of committing crimes against humanity by not eliminating fossil fuels. She told us that we are taking away her happiness, and the happiness of her entire generation and of generations to come, eliminating any value to her life, while we remain oblivious to the destruction we perpetrate. Greta is using "descriptions of the reality of Hell to invoke psychosomatic reactions of terror in (her) audience."[848]

Greta's statements seem strong and powerful, and, in her voice, they are frightening. But since there is no scientific basis for claiming global warming is destroying the Earth or that human use of fossil fuels is causing significant global warming, her statements are basically religious beliefs that confirm the beliefs of other Activists. This is not a call to "follow the science" or even to show compassion to one's fellow humans or to animals and plants. Greta is disconnected from science. She is preaching, not educating. Her sermons are the opposite of reality and contrary to the history of Earth and nature.

Greta is no different from the many politicians and writers who use fear of global warming to build successful careers. Their strategy, which has proven to be so effective, is to use whatever extreme weather event might be occurring to remind us of the horrors of global warming, in hopes of converting us to their faith. They ask us to ignore history and science.

The Religion of Climate Change

You have already seen numerous examples that the Activists fear of climate change is religious in nature and contrary to science. Even though it is contrary to reality, they scold us for not believing in major accelerations of sea-levels, more dangerous hurricanes, mass animal extinctions, and forest fire disasters. Since these are beliefs unsupported by empirical evidence, it is fair to call them religious beliefs.

One reasonable definition of a religious belief is when a sane person misinterprets a scientific fact to produce a conclusion that is pure nonsense. A fair example of Activists spouting nonsense is their belief that the fact that global warming has been mostly at night and in the winter is undesirable. It is factually true that warming during the days and summers has been about .25°C lower than the warming during the nights and winter. [849] My guess is that to most sane people, this is more desirable than the opposite. How blessed we have been!

Here are some typical Activist comments on warmer nights:

- The *New York Times* writes, "Nights are warming faster than days and here is why that is dangerous."[850]
- "High nighttime temperatures can increase the risk of heat-related hospitalizations and deaths …can also worsen wildfire conditions …When it is really hot at night …it puts more physiological strain on your body."[851]
- *The Guardian,* which boasts that "millions can benefit from their truthfulness," falsely tells us that higher nighttime temperatures are "exacerbating the dangers of heatwaves that already kill more Americans than any other natural disaster."[852]

Winter temperatures have increased more than summer. One report tells us that "the month of December (in Maine and Alaska) is now 5°F warmer than it (had been)."[853] Warmer winters in Maine and Alaska should sound very good to the residents. Since global warming has been only a fraction of 5°F, it seems reasonable that the summers are probably a bit cooler. Sounds good to me!

One final example: *The Guardian* tells us that "warmer winters can cause as much havoc as hotter summers," and milder winters can cause catastrophic weather and increase the probability of violent events like heat waves in summer. Furthermore, *The Guardian* alerts us to expect more mosquito bites and possible West Nile disease.[854]

When Sam Johnson, the leader of Johnson Wax (now S.C Johnson and Son) was asked how Raid (the world's leading bug killer) was doing, he would say, "Raid is doing terrifically. The Bugs are winning." Of course, he was kidding. The problem with these Activists is that they are *not* kidding! They want us to be afraid that a fraction of one degree of temperature increase in the winter is going to cause more mosquito bites and possibly bring on West Nile Disease. How dumb do they think we are? Why would they want us to believe this type of myth that only a publication like a satirical humor site like *The Babylon Bee* would consider publishing?

If you open Google's first page of possible climate change benefits from increases in warmer nights and winters, you will find almost no support. The Activists tell us that we are not going to benefit from a .25°C increase in winter and nighttime temperatures, and that our bodies would benefit from cooler winters and cooler nights. How does that make any sense? Let's give them credit for creative thinking, but these are foolish warnings made by Activists to frighten us. In many respects, this is beyond religion and appears to reek of dishonesty.

Mental Illness

Greta says:

- "People are suffering. People are dying. Entire ecosystems are collapsing."[855]
- "You have taken away my dreams and my childhood with your empty words."[856]
- "What we do or don't do right now will affect my entire life, and the lives of my children and grandchildren."[857]
- "We children are doing this because we want our hopes and dreams back."[858]

These statements by Greta convey the message that our alleged failure to address global warming is *mentally disturbing* to young people around the world. Global warming isn't only a scientific or economic issue, Greta is saying. It is a psychological hurt as well.

The American Psychiatric Association (APA) claims global warming must be causing mental health problems because its leaders believe the claim made by the U.N. that climate change creates 20 million climate refugees yearly due to floods, storms, forest fires, and extreme temperatures.[859] The APA tells us that 50% of Americans believe that global warming causes anxiety and severe mental health disorders.[860][861]

In its writing, *How Climate Change Impacts Physical, Mental and Community Health,* [862] the APA claims that the global warming of 1°C during the past 100 years injured our (1) physical health by causing more heat-related diseases; (2) our mental health because it strains our social relationships; and (3) our community health by causing more violence and crime. [863]

Can you imagine how much more severe the APA would predict that our heat-related diseases, the strain on our social relationships, and additional crime and violence we would have if temperatures increased another 1°C?

The problem is that there are no more floods, storms, or forest fires than in the past. There are no *climate refugees.* That's just a myth.[864] The bombardment of the public by media reports and stories claiming that almost any extreme weather condition is a disaster caused by man-made global warming is not consistent with reality. It is the media reports, not global warming, that causes "anxiety, depression, secondary trauma and other psychological conditions."[865]

Happiness and Unhappiness

Throughout this chapter, I have intentionally ignored Greta's autism disorder, as this is claimed to be both a problem and an asset for her communication.[866] There are reports that Greta is not a happy person.[867] Why would anyone want to take advice on how to live from a person who is so unhappy? And exactly how does she help her 2.5 million Facebook followers find happiness when she threatens certain catastrophe by 2030? How can children be happy when they are told they are complicit in the mass destruction of the planet when they use fossil fuels?

It is truly unfortunate that the mass media, our government, the U.N., and so many teachers and university professors don't provide a more positive message to today's youth. After all, we are living longer lives, there is less poverty, humanity is better educated, and all this has happened during the past 100 years when the average global surface temperature increased 1°C.

As Carlos Castaneda wrote, "We either make ourselves miserable or we make ourselves happy. The amount of work is the same."[868]

We all need happiness and confidence. Deepak Chopra has told us "success in life could be defined as the continued expansion of happiness and the progressive realization of worthy goals."[869] Global warming is an imaginary problem and there is no reason to waste huge amounts of time, energy, resources, and money on non-existent problems.[870] When we allow ourselves to struggle against these imaginary issues, we suffer from helplessness, hopelessness, and quiet desperation and allow ourselves to become fearful and insecure. We might as well be struggling against the universe.

So let us accept the truth that the weather and climate during our lives has been wonderfully supportive of human progress and the natural world. The Earth has never been cleaner than it is today. Our goal should be that, as Climate Realists, we will pursue the continued expansion of happiness and strive to realize worthy goals.

No Quiz or Fake News for this Chapter. Just me thanking you for considering the thoughts I have expressed in this book and my hope that you found here something of value.

Summary

- Greta Thunberg, the most effective and persuasive Climate Activist, with great emotion and religious intensity, continually shames us with false claims of mass animal extinction and future climate catastrophes from fossil fuels. As the Babylon Bee predicts, we only have a few years left before she revises her time schedule to give us another 12 years before we suffer from the "existential threat of our time," which is the climate catastrophe that exists in her mind.

- The truth is that we have been blessed with a climate that has been amazingly consistent for 100 years.

- As Climate Realists, we should pursue the continued expansion of happiness and strive to realize worthy goals.

Chapter 10
Conclusion

"God helps those who help themselves"
(Ben Franklin, Poor Richard's Almanac – 1757)
(Algernon Sydney, Discourses Concerning Government – 1698)

The author explains why the belief that climate change is a problem that must be immediately addressed is false, biased, and dangerous. The author suggests what we should tell our grandchildren if we are wrong, why he wrote this book, and makes his final request to you, the reader.

The Story of Chelm

According to Jewish folklore, the Lord sent an angel with a sack full of foolish souls to be evenly distributed throughout the Earth, but the angel fell and spilled them all in a small Polish town called Chelm. Shortly thereafter, a heated argument occurred among the people of Chelm related to the question of which was more important: the Sun or the Moon. People were equally divided into two sides. The controversy became heated, and the people of Chelm decided to ask the chief rabbi for resolution.

The chief rabbi told the people this issue was so very difficult that it would require one week of intense study to resolve. A week later, the chief rabbi emerged and announced his decision. "It is obvious," he said. "The Moon is more important because it sheds light at night when light is needed, but the Sun only provides light during the day, a time already blessed with sufficient light."

Much of the people in Chelm then agreed with the chief rabbi. In fact, there arose a 97 percent consensus that the Moon was the more important celestial body. It quickly became settled science in Chelm, supported by official fact checkers, and only ignorant "Moon deniers" believed the Sun was more important than the Moon.

Those who support the Climate Activists in their fear of global warming and climate change have much in common with the people of Chelm. Instead of basing their decisions upon scientific and empirical facts, these people listened to an authority that based their decisions on bad assumptions and ignored relevant scientific criteria, were ignorant of it, or were so biased that they produced shoddy science. Thus, the Activists, instead of predicting sea level rise based on actual measurements of past consistent sea rises, used computer models which included their opinions of how much glacial ice melted during the past 120 years to generate guesses guided by bias, rather than forecasts based on science. Then, these "climate experts" were heralded by the media as geniuses who were able to create millions of lines of computer code to predict with "high confidence" the catastrophes that would destroy us. Meanwhile, rather than considering the validity of other views based on real science, the Activists ignore and ridicule those with contrary views.

Certainly, many Climate Activists are good people. Most are very smart, well-educated, and probably want the best for everyone. However, history has not confirmed their predictions of global warming and climate change. In addition to their predictions, including that the Earth would warm several degrees during the recent past and that the seas would rise at an accelerating rate, they have predicted that coral reefs would disappear, that many fish species and one-third of all animals, including the polar bear, would become extinct, and that forest fires and major storms would become more frequent and severe. *All these predictions were wrong and are contradicted by empirical historical results.*

Fear and Misery vs. Happiness and Goal Realization

I hope my book has provided empirical and scientific knowledge that successfully refutes the false arguments of Climate Activists. In my view, they are emperors without clothes, pretending to be wise leaders with impressive titles and specialized knowledge, but offering nothing but unjustified fear, misery, and unhappiness.

John Keats wrote, "A thing of beauty is a joy forever" and "beauty is truth, truth beauty. That is all ye know on Earth and all ye need to know."[871] There is true beauty when you know the truth.

Deepak Chopra has written that success in life is the continued expansion of happiness and the realization of worthy goals.[872] How can we be happy if we believe we are most certainly doomed in 12, 20, or 50 years? Climate Activists warn us that the "excess use" of fossil fuels will destroy our world. They guide us to become unhappy prisoners of helplessness, hopelessness and quiet desperation. They want us to worry and concentrate on eliminating problems that do not exist. They are wasting their time and their lives, and they want us to do the same.[873]

In writing this book, I found that the climate change on Earth during the past 100 years has been remarkably minimal and remarkably stable. The 5 years ending in 2021 were less than 1/5 of a degree warmer than the previous 25 years. It is this consistency in weather rather than changes that have been so exceptional.

How blessed we are!

Here is what I learned in the course of writing this book:

- Carbon dioxide (CO_2) plays only a small role in determining the surface temperature of the Earth or in changing weather.
- Sea levels have risen by about the same amount yearly for 100 years.
- The frequency and severity of major climatic events, including hurricanes, tornadoes, flooding, and droughts, have not increased.

- The only major animal extinctions were caused by human activities such as hunting, over-fishing, and development, not by climate change.

- Coral reefs thrive and remain beautiful where the water is clean despite "acidification" or rising seawater temperatures.

- Replacing fossil fuels with alternatives, such as solar and wind power, would be enormously expensive and probably require a major reduction in our energy consumption.+

What if We Are Wrong?

I mentioned earlier that my wife and I promoted a debate on global warming at our alma mater. The professor who asserted that global warming
is a major threat did a fine job representing his position and most of the
students agreed with him that sustainability is a major problem. At the end
of the debate, he asked an important question, *"What are you going to tell
your children if you are wrong?"* This is what I would propose for both sides.

An Apology by the Author, a Climate Realist

I am very sorry! I followed the science to the best of my ability and believed
climate change on Earth would continue just as it had for the previous
100 *years. Since the dawn of the Industrial Revolution, the Earth had warmed
abo*ut 1°C, while wealth creation, longevity, educational improvement,
and reduction in poverty had all been greater than in any previous time in
recorded history. The world was becoming cleaner and greener. I thought
one degree of additional warmth would have a similar effect and certainly
cause no serious damage. I admit I was wrong.

But here's the thing. Even though the Earth heated up significantly,
we saved trillions of dollars that would otherwise have been wasted com-
plying with regulations and subsidizing technological dead-ends, lost to
corruption, and collected in taxes. Those dollars were invested in things
that created prosperity and happiness.

That said, I should have listened more carefully to Climate Activists
who said we were destroying the Earth by our excessive use of fossil fuels.
I wanted to encourage people to be happy and confident because happy
and confident people make the best decisions. I still think that was the
right message. Sad, guilt-ridden, and frightened people don't make wise
choices and don't hand down to future generations the tools and resources
they need to succeed.

I saw how Al Gore had falsely predicted many animals which he
claimed were headed toward extinction were not, and I never believed
predictions that thousands of species of fish and land animals were headed

toward extinction. After all, as of when I wrote this book, there was no sign of animal extinction due to global warming anywhere. Similarly, I knew that most forest fires were caused by human activities such as arson and power lines, not by global warming, and there had been no increase in the number or severity of forest fires; that hurricanes had not increased or become significantly more intense during the past century; that sea-levels had been consistent for 100 years; and that there was no evidence whatsoever that people would need to migrate from warming to cooler climates.

But apparently, the past was not a reliable guide to the future. Climate models predicting sharp breaks from all of these long-term trends were more accurate than I thought. Once again, I admit I was wrong.

An Apology by a Climate Activist

I am sorry! I am very sorry we wasted huge amounts of money, time, and energy trying to address a problem I thought existed but did not. I knew it would cost trillions of dollars, which it did, and for those trillions, we accomplished nothing.

We caused billions of people to be worried and scared and blamed them for contributing to the destruction of the Earth when it was really our arrogance and poor scientific forecasting that was damaging. Instead of allowing people to spend their money on what they thought best, we taxed and regulated them and wasted enormous funds which could have been used to generate more universal prosperity, improve lifestyles, reduce poverty, improve education, cure diseases and contribute to their happiness. Our efforts resulted in enormous additional debt, which you and all future generations will be responsible to repay or live with.

We should have followed history and looked at real-world data rather than the output of computer models, which we now realize just echoed our highly biased thinking. Virtually all of our predictions of more hurricanes, forest fires, floods, and droughts were overstated. The global warming that did occur caused no damage. The planet is as healthy and safe as it has ever been.

We called those who disagreed with us "climate deniers" and "science deniers," criticized them personally, and sued them for their scientific truths. Our arrogance resulted in preventing their ideas from being heard because our arrogance told us that our ideas were the only good ones. We damaged and even destroyed the careers of many scientists who were simply pursuing the truth. As a result of our efforts, we irreparably damaged the reputation of science and set back scientific discovery by decades. I am truly sorry.

My Request to You

My request is that you share this message with those you love, those you meet, and especially those who have been taught to believe that global warming and climate change is the "existential crisis of our time." I have tried to provide historical and scientific facts which you can use to inform others with the scientific truths that the climate is changing and it is good! Let me thank you in advance for any effort you make to spread the truth about global warming and climate change.

As a starving author, I suggest you buy additional copies of my book to give to all your friends and relatives and encourage them to read it. You can buy copies at Amazon.com or at the website, **www.climatechangeus. com.** I assure you that not only will this expand their knowledge of global warming, but it unquestionably will improve your relationship with all of your relatives and friends, and they will be forever grateful to you.

Any purchaser of 50 copies of my book at retail will also receive for free a portion of my U.S. stamp collection, which I am currently selling. If you have family members and friends who aren't likely to read an entire book about global warming, direct them to my *Original Climate Change Cheat Guide,* which is very cheap and provides a short summary of many significant climate change issues.

Finally, I want to thank you for reading my book and I hope that you have found some value in it.

ENDNOTES

CHAPTER 1

1   Chandler, David L. "Climate Myths: It's Been Far Warmer in the Past, What's the Big Deal?" New Scientist. New Scientist, May 16, 2007. https://www.newscientist.com/article/dn11647-climate-myths-its-been-far-warmer-in-the-past-whats-the-big-deal/

2   "Climate Science Glossary." Skeptical Science. https://www.skepticalscience.com/how-blogs-distort-sci-info-polar-bears-arctic.html

3   See Google: "Einstein quotation on consensus"

4   The consensus myth didn't begin with Cook et al. in 2013. NASA cites multiple articles written prior to Cook's article. NASA 2018. Scientific consensus: "Earth's climate is warming." Also see Climate change Reconsidered II: Fossil Fuels (CCR), pages 274-279. The EPA also cites Oreskes 2004, Doran and Zimmerman 2009, and Anderegg et al., 2010 (citations follow). Cook, John, Dana Nuccitelli, Sarah A. Green, Mark Richardson, Bärbel Winkler, Rob Painting, Robert Way, Peter Jacobs, and Andrew Skuce. "Quantifying the consensus on anthropogenic global warming in the scientific literature." *Environmental research letters*, 8, no. 2 (2013): 024024.
"Climate Change Reconsidered II: Fossil Fuels." Climate Change Reconsidered. Nongovernmental International Panel on Climate Change, May 22, 2019. https://climatechangereconsidered.org/climate-change-reconsidered-ii-fossil-fuels/
Oreskes, Naomi. "Undeniable global warming." *Washington Post* 26 (2004).
Doran, Peter T., and Maggie Kendall Zimmerman. "Examining the scientific consensus on climate change." *Eos, Transactions American Geophysical Union* 90, no. 3 (2009): 22-23.
Anderegg, William RL, James W. Prall, Jacob Harold, and Stephen H. Schneider. "Expert credibility in climate change." *Proceedings of the National Academy of Sciences* 107, no. 27 (2010): 12107-12109.

5   This is an article of monumental importance, but believe me, it is a real snoozer. "Skeptical Science." Wikipedia. Wikimedia Foundation, October 22, 2022. https://en.wikipedia.org/wiki/Skeptical_Science

6   Note that Cook's team read only abstracts, not actual articles, and abstracts often contain statements and key words that are unrelated to what the experiment or study actually found. Many of these studies just mention climate change in passing (from Joe Bast, past president of Heartland institute).

7   "97% Global Warming Consensus Paper Surpasses Half a Million Downloads." Skeptical Science. https://skepticalscience.com/cook-2013-surpasses-500k-downloads.html
For additional Commentary on Consensus, see 8 below.

8   "Skeptical Science Study Finds 97% Consensus on Human-Caused Global Warming in the Peer-Reviewed Literature." Skeptical Science. https://skepticalscience.com/97-percent-consensus-cook-et-al-2013.html https://skepticalscience.com/97-percent-consensus-cook-et-al-2013.html

9   Wrightstone, Gregory. *Inconvenient Facts: The Science that Al Gore Doesn't Want You to Know*. Silver Crown Productions, LLC, 2017. p. 59, and replies by the Viscount Monckton of Brenchley to questions from Elias Hazou, Cyprus Mai, January 2019.

10   Wrightstone, Gregory. *Inconvenient Facts: The Science that Al Gore Doesn't Want You to Know*. Silver Crown Productions, LLC, 2017, p. 63 and Maibach 2016 Center for Climate Communication, George Mason University.

11   Mandia, Scott. "Global Warming: Man or Myth." Global warming misinformation - consensus isn't science (What about Galileo?), 2018. https://www.sunysuffolk.edu/explore-academics/faculty-and-staff/faculty-websites/scott-mandia/global_warming/global_warming_misinformation_galileo.html

12   "Climate Change Reconsidered II: Fossil Fuels,"p. 210. See Note 4 for source information.

13   Oregon Petition. "Global Warming Petition Project." http://www.petitionproject.org/index.php Note: 9,000 of the signatories had PhDs.

14   "Did 30,000 Scientists Declare That Climate Change Is a Hoax? - Quora." https://www.quora.com/Did-30-000-scientists-declare-that-climate-change-is-a-hoax

15   Ibid.

16   Oregon Petition. "Global Warming Petition Project." http://www.petitionproject.org/index.php

17   As of April 2021, the rate of increase during 2020 did not reflect any reduction in measurable emissions due to the coronavirus pandemic. Stein, Theo. "Rise of Carbon Dioxide Unabated." Welcome to NOAA Research, June 4, 2020. https://research.noaa.gov/article/ArtMID/587/ArticleID/2636/Rise-of-carbon-dioxide-unabated

18   The rise in atmospheric CO_2 levels is due to the "outgassing" of CO_2 from oceans as the planet slowly warms from the last Ice Age as well as human emissions. (Joe Bast, Heartland Institute)

19   Moskvitch, Katia. "Dinosaur Era Had 5 Times Today's CO2." LiveScience. Purch, March 24, 2014. https://www.livescience.com/44330-jurassic-dinosaur-carbon-dioxide.html

20   Gore, Al. *An inconvenient truth: The crisis of global warming*. Penguin, 2006. p. 24.

21   "It's Water Vapor, Not the CO2." American Chemical Society. https://www.acs.org/content/acs/en/climate-science/climatesciencenarratives/its-water-vapor-not-the-co2.html

22   "Overview of Greenhouse Gases." EPA. Environmental Protection Agency, 2022. https://www.epa.gov/ghgemissions/overview-greenhouse-gases

23   Cornell, Brent. "Greenhouse Gases." BioNinja, 2022. https://ib.bioninja.com.au/standard-level/topic-4-ecology/44-climate-change/greenhouse-gases.html

24   In 2007, in a 5-4 decision the Supreme Court ruled that CO_2 was a pollutant. This allowed the EPA to control the gas mileage in cars. Soure: "Is CO2 a Pollutant?." Skeptical Science, 2017. https://skepticalscience.com/co2-pollutant-advanced.htm

       Gore, Al. *An inconvenient truth: The crisis of global warming*, p. 24. See Note 20 for source information.

       "It's Water Vapor, Not the CO2." American Chemical Society. See Note 21 for more information.

       "Overview of Greenhouse Gases." See Note 22 for source information.

       "Greenhouse Gases." See Note 23 for source information.

       "Is CO2 a Pollutant?." See Note 24 for source information. In 2007, in a 5-4 decision the Supreme Court made rulings on fossil fuels. Of course, if CO_2 is a pollutant then every time we breathe, we are polluting the air. This was clearly a political definition and not a scientific one because CO_2 in the atmosphere has never caused injury or sickness to any human. This would also make water vapor, which is over 90% of greenhouse gases, a pollutant and every time we boil water, we are polluting.

25   CO_2 occurs naturally in the air and within almost all bodies of water. About 96% of the carbon dioxide in the air comes from natural sources (outgassing from oceans, weathering of limestone, and volcanic activity) and only about 4% comes from human activity. The natural flow of CO_2 between the air, oceans, and rocks and sediments dwarfs the human contribution of CO_2 into the air.
       "Climate change Reconsidered II: Fossil Fuels,"p. 132. See Note 4 for source information.

26   "CO$_2$ was considered for a time to be a deadly poison and will be remembered as the greatest mass delusion in the history of the world" – Richard Lindzen, MIT Physics and former head of the National Academy of Sciences.

27   Friedman, Daniel J. "Co2 Carbon Dioxide Gas Exposure Limits." Inspectapedia, 2021. https://inspectapedia.com/hazmat/Carbon_Dioxide_Exposure_Limits.php

28   "Carbon Dioxide." Wikimedia Foundation, 2022. https://en.wikipedia.org/wiki/Carbon_dioxide

29   "Climate Change Reconsidered II: Fossil Fuels,"p. 474. See Note 4 for source information.

30   See Note 28.

31   See Note 28.

32   Soon, Willie, Sallie L. Baliunas, Arthur B. Robinson, and Zachary W. Robinson. "Environmental effects of increased atmospheric carbon dioxide." *Climate research* 13, no. 2 (1999): 149-164. https://www.int-res.com/abstracts/cr/v13/n2/p149-164

33   "Willie Soon." Wikipedia. Wikimedia Foundation, 2022. https://en.wikipedia.org/wiki/Willie_Soon

34   Google Search on world temperatures using the following link, https://www.google.com/search?q=world+temperatures+april+2020&ie=UTF-8&oe=UTF-8&hl=en-us&client=safari

35   Le Quéré, Corinne, Robert B. Jackson, Matthew W. Jones, Adam JP Smith, Sam Abernethy, Robbie M. Andrew, Anthony J. De-Gol et al. "Temporary reduction in daily global CO 2 emissions during the COVID-19 forced confinement." *Nature climate change* 10, no. 7 (2020): 647-653. https://www.nature.com/articles/s41558-020-0797-x

36   Lomborg, Bjorn. "How the Climate Elite Spread Misery." *Wall Street Journal*, Jul 22, 2022.

37   "Global Temperature Anomaly Graph." Wikimedia Commons, 2020. https://commons.wikimedia.org/wiki/File:Global_Temperature_Anomaly.svg

38   Berkeley Earth

39   All references agree. Look at Google, Bing, or ask any scientist or non-scientist anywhere else will confirm this.

40   Rohde, Robert. "Global Temperature Report for 2018." Berkeley Earth, January 20, 2021. http://berkeleyearth.org/2018-temperatures/; also see https://www.carbonbrief.org/factcheck-no-global-warming-has-not-paused-over-the-past-eight-years/ and https://www.nytimes.com/2021/01/08/climate/hottest-year-ever.html

41   New York City hottest day - Google Search

42   "Miami Florida Climate." ClimateSpy, 2022. https://www.climatespy.com/climate/summary/united-states/florida/miami-intl#:~:text=The%20hottest%20day%20on%20record,recorded%20on%20January%2022%20 1985

43   Jordan, Jay R. "Looking Back at the Hottest Day in Houston History." Houston Chronicle, July 28, 2021. https://www.chron.com/weather/article/houston-hottest-day-record-forecast-weather-109-16343644.php

44   Google search for hottest day in San Francisco. https://www.google.com/search?q=hottest+day+ever+in+san+francisco&ie=UTF-8&oe=UTF-8&hl=en-us&client=safari

45   This reveals an important issue in the climate debate: nobody lives in the "average global climate." Climate is a local phenomenon, and at any given time some areas are warming while others are cooling. A one-size-fits-all scientific theory or public policy response doesn't work when it comes to climate change. (Joe Bast, Founder of Heartland Institute , private communication)

46   McNerthney, Casey. "Heat Wave Broils Western Washington, Shattering Seattle and Regional Temperature Records on June 28, 2021." HistoryLink, 2021. https://www.historylink.org/File/21266

47   "Global Temperature Report for 2018." See Note 40 for source information.

48   HadCRUT4 data, May 2016 to January 2021

49   "Why Did the Climate Cool in the Mid-20th Century?" Skeptical Science, 2015. https://skepticalscience.com/global-cooling-mid-20th-century.htm

50   Same reference as Note 49.

51   Wrightstone, Gregory. *Inconvenient Facts: The Science that Al Gore Doesn't Want You to Know*. Silver Crown Productions, LLC, 2017, p. 25.

52   Michaels, Patrick J., and Paul C. Knappenberger. *Lukewarming: The new climate science that changes everything*. Cato Institute, 2016, p. 145.

53   Friedan, Betty. "The Coming Ice Age." Harper's Magazine , May 9, 2019. https://harpers.org/archive/1958/09/the coming ice age/

54   van der Schrier, Gerard, EJ M. van den Besselaar, A. M. G. Klein Tank, and Ge Verver. "Monitoring European average temperature based on the E-OBS gridded data set." *Journal of Geophysical Research: Atmospheres* 118, no. 11 (2013): 5120-5135. https://agupubs.onlinelibrary.wiley.com/doi/full/10.1002/jgrd.50444

55   Pearce, Lara. "This Is the Perfect Temperature for Happiness." Huffington Post, November 27, 2017. https://www.huffingtonpost.com.au/2017/11/27/this-is-the-perfect-temperature-for-being-happy-and-social-study-finds_a_23288718/

56   Worrall, Eric. "Claim: The Optimum Average Annual Temperature for Humans Is 13C (55F)." Watts Up With That?, October 22, 2015. https://wattsupwiththat.com/2015/10/21/claim-optimum-average-annual-temperature-for-humans-is-13c-55f/

57   Nuccitelli, Dana. "Scott Pruitt Insincerely Asked What's Earth's Ideal Temperature. Scientists Answer | Dana Nuccitelli." The Guardian. Guardian News and Media, January 17, 2018. https://www.theguardian.com/environment/climate-consensus-97-per-cent/2018/jan/17/scott-pruitt-insincerely-asked-whats-earths-ideal-temperature-scientists-answer

58   Google Search for lowest temperatures in Alaska. https://www.google.com/search?q=lowest+temperaturein+alaska&ie=UTF-8&oe=UTF-8&hl=en-us&client=safari

59   Bradt Guides. "When and Where to Visit - Burkina Faso." Bradt Guides, February 10, 2021. https://www.bradtguides.com/destinations/africa/burkina-faso/when-and-where-to-visit/
Google Search for highest temperatures in Burkino Faso. https://www.google.com/search?q=burkino+faso+highest+temperature&ie=UTF-8&oe=UTF-8&hl=en-us&client=safari

60   Monckton, Christopher. "Climate Misinformation by Source." Skeptical Science, 2022. https://skepticalscience.com/Monckton_Myths_arg.htm
"Christopher Monckton." Wikipedia. Wikimedia Foundation, October 26, 2022. https://en.wikipedia.org/wiki/Christopher_Monckton,_3rd_Viscount_Monckton_of_Brenchley

61   Milwaukee Journal Sentinel pg. 6A 5/5/2020

62   Xu, Chi, Timothy A. Kohler, Timothy M. Lenton, Jens-Christian Svenning, and Marten Scheffer. "Future of the human climate niche." *Proceedings of the National Academy of Sciences* 117, no. 21 (2020): 11350-11355. https://www.pnas.org/content/early/2020/04/28/1910114117

63   Burkina Faso map - Yahoo Image Search Results

64   "Burkina Faso Population Graph." Wikimedia Commons, 2016. https://upload.wikimedia.org/wikipedia/commons/a/a1/Burkina_Faso_population.svg

65   "Anthony Watts – IntelliWeather" <awatts@intelliweather.com>

66   Hayhoe, Katharine. "*What's the Big Deal With a Few Degrees?*" YouTube, 2019. https://www.youtube.com/watch?v=6cRCbgTA_78

67   Worrall, Eric. "Claim: The Optimum Average Annual Temperature for Humans Is 13C (55F)." See Note 56 for source information.

68   Rohde, Robert. "Global Temperature Report for 2018." See Note 40 for source information.

69   Spector, Joseph. "I Leave NY: 1.4 Million Left for Other States since 2010. Here's Where They Moved." Democrat and Chronicle. New York State Team, January 3, 2020. https://www.democratandchronicle.com/story/news/politics/albany/2020/01/03/new-yorkers-leave-for-florida-where-to-move/2795538001/

70   "Average Annual Temperature for Each US State." Average Annual Temperatures by USA State - Current Results, 2022. https://www.currentresults.com/Weather/US/average-annual-state-temperatures.php

71   Michaels, Patrick J., Robert C. Balling Jr, Russell S. Vose, and Paul C. Knappenberger. "Analysis of trends in the variability of daily and monthly historical temperature measurements." *Climate Research* 10, no. 1 (1998): 27-33. https://www.int-res.com/abstracts/cr/v10/n1/p27-33/

72   Lomborg, Bjorn. Global Warming Thread. https://twitter.com/BjornLomborg/status/1418916412802965511/photo/1

73   Ciscar 2009 predicted that by 2080, if significant global warming were to occur, the number of deaths attributed to cold weather in the European Union would fall by 100,000. Also see Wrightstone, Gregory. *Inconvenient Facts: The Science that Al Gore Doesn't Want You to Know*. Silver Crown Productions, LLC, 2017, p. 82.

74   Gasparini 2015 studied 74 million deaths in 13 countries between 1985 and 2012 and concluded that only 1 in 250 deaths were related to heat, but 1 in 20 deaths were related to cold. https://www.sciencedirect.com/science/ article/pii/S0140673614621140

75   Jsonline.com 6/2/21 pg. 11A

76   There is some uncertainty in the planet's temperature history to support the null hypothesis that temperatures have not increased at all for many years; and whatever warming we have had for the past 40 years is due to the El Niño effect. (See a detailed scientific study by Thomas K. Bjorklund of the University of Houston titled "170 Years of Earth Surface Temperature Data Show No Evidence of Significant Warming") Bjorklund, Thomas K. "170 Years of Earth Surface Temperature Data Show No Evidence of Significant Warming." 2020. https://www.uh.edu/nsm/earth-atmospheric/people/faculty/tom-bjorklund/global-warming-manuscript_mar5_final-draft-with-addendum_revised-mar24.pdf

77   Einhorn email sent on 6/5/21 7:30 AM

CHAPTER 2

78   Search on movie and audience statistics for An Inconvenient Truth. https://en.wikipedia.org/wiki/An_Inconvenient_Truth

79   Search on movie and audience statistics for An Inconvenient Truth. https://www.google.com/search?q=average+cost+of+movie+in+2008&ie=UTF-8&oe=UTF-8&hl=en-us&client=safari

80   Rettner, Rachael. "Al Gore's Movie 'an Inconvenient Truth' Says Sea Levels Could Rise up to 20 Feet. Is This True?" Scienceline, March 5, 2010. https://scienceline.org/2008/12/ask-rettner-sea-level-rise-al-gore-an-inconvenient-truth/.

81   Search on truth basis for An Inconvenient Truth. https://en.wikipedia.org/wiki/An_Inconvenient_Truth#Scientific_basis

82   Search for average cost for a move. https://www.google.com/search?q=average+cost+of+movie+in+2008&ie=UTF-8&oe=UTF-8&hl=en-us&client=safari

83   Gore, Al. *An inconvenient truth: The crisis of global warming*, p. 18, see Note 20 for source information

84   Associated Press, June 30,1989. Quoted in Michaels, Patrick J., and Paul C. Knappenberger. *Lukewarming: The new climate science that changes everything*. Cato Institute, 2016. p. 179.

85   Graham, Tim. "Beware the 'Green Fraud' and the Climate Lockdown." CNSNews.com, 2021. https://www.cnsnews.com/commentary/tim-graham/beware-green-fraud-and-climate-lockdown

86   McDougall, Dan. "Sleeping in Fields, Eating Ice and Dirt." The Guardian. Guardian News and Media, October 11, 2005. https://www.theguardian.com/environment/2005/oct/12/naturaldisasters.climatechange

87   Ibid.

88   "Global Climate in 2015-2019: Climate Change Accelerates." World Meteorological Organization, September 24, 2019. https://public.wmo.int/en/media/press-release/global-climate-2015-2019-climate-change-accelerates
Special Summary Report: *IPCC Special Report on Ocean and Cryosphere in a Changing Climate*. https://www.ipcc.ch/srocc/chapter/technical-summary/; https://www.ipcc.ch/srocc/chapter/chapter-4-sea-level-rise-and-implications-for-low-lying-islands-coasts-and-communities/

89   The Cornell Chronicle. Cornell research the Journal Land Use Policy, July 2017. Blaine Friedlander, June 19, 2017.

90   The biggest sea level calamity I could find was that during the past 20 years, three uninhabited Solomon Islands sank 5 inches and are now under water.https://www.cnn.com/2016/05/10/world/pacific-solomon-islands-disappear/index.html

91   Penn State Source. https://www.e-education.psu.edu/Earth107/node/1506

92   "USGCRP Indicator Details." GlobalChange.gov. https://www.globalchange.gov/browse/indicators/global-sea-level-rise

93   Research on global sea levels. Holgate, S. J. "On the decadal rates of sea level change during the twentieth century." *Geophysical research letters* 34, no. 1 (2007).
Houston, James Robert, and Robert George Dean. "Sea-level acceleration based on US tide gauges and extensions of previous global-gauge analyses." *Journal of Coastal Research* 27, no. 3 (2011): 409-417.
Watson, P. J. "Is there evidence yet of acceleration in mean sea level rise around mainland Australia?." *Journal of Coastal Research* 27, no. 2 (2011): 368-377.

94   Quiñones , Laura. "Earth's Oceans and Frozen Spaces Paying Price for 'Taking the Heat of Global Warming' | 1UN News." United Nations. United Nations. 2019. https://news.un.org/en/story/2019/09/1047392

95   "Sea Level Resources." Climate Resilience Collaborative, 2022. http://www.soest.hawaii.edu/coasts/sealevel/ "SWOT Simulated Products: 2 New Datasets L2 and L3." Home: Aviso+, 2022. http://www.aviso.oceanobs.com/en/news/ocean-indicators/mean-sea-level/

96   The Heartland Institute Report 2017, by geophysicist Dennis Hedke. Also locally, sea levels may be higher or lower due to land subsidence (sinking), compaction of sediments or isostatic rebound: David Legates at the University of Delaware.

97   Burnett, Sterling. "Sea Level Rise Not Accelerating, New Study Shows." The Heartland Institute, 2019. https://www.heartland.org/news-opinion/news/sea-level-rise-not-accelerating-new-study-shows

98   Search on tides and current NOAA government

99   Sea Level Trends - NOAA Tides & Currents. "Sea Level Trends - NOAA Tides & Currents." https://tidesandcurrents.noaa.gov/sltrends/sltrends_station.shtml?id=050-141

100   In this chapter, I have identified about a dozen specific shoreline cities. I have looked at many cities and have never found one which had significant acceleration in its sea levels over time.

101   Communication with Baylor Fox-Kemper 9/12/2021

102   Some claim slower growth in Sea Levels: Sea levels have risen for over 200 years by an almost constant level (about 1 inch every 10 years) (Jevrejeva 2008).
Jevrejeva, S., John C. Moore, Aslak Grinsted, and Philip L. Woodworth. "Recent global sea level acceleration started over 200 years ago?." *Geophysical Research Letters* 35, no. 8 (2008).

103   Honore, Marcel. "A $15 Billion Price Tag To Protect Hawaii Highways From Climate Change." Honolulu Civil Beat, April 4, 2018. https://www.civilbeat.org/2018/04/a-15-billion-price-tag-to-protect-hawaii-highways-from-climate-change/

104   Caccamise, Dana J., Mark A. Merrifield, Michael Bevis, James Foster, Yvonne L. Firing, Mark S. Schenewerk, Frederick W. Taylor, and Donald A. Thomas. "Sea level rise at Honolulu and Hilo, Hawaii: GPS estimates of differential land motion." *Geophysical Research Letters* 32, no. 3 (2005). https://agupubs.onlinelibrary.wiley.com/doi/full/10.1029/2004GL021380

105   Sea Level Trends - NOAA Tides & Currents. "Sea Level Trends - NOAA Tides & Currents." 2022. https://tidesandcurrents.noaa.gov/sltrends/sltrends_station.shtml?id=1617760

106   Sea Level Trends - NOAA Tides & Currents. "Sea Level Trends - NOAA Tides & Currents." 2022. https://tidesandcurrents.noaa.gov/sltrends/sltrends_station.shtml?stnid=8723170

107   CFACT letter 5/24/2020, p 5

108   SeaLevelRise.org. "Florida's Sea Level Is Rising." Sea Level Rise. https://sealevelrise.org/states/florida/

109   Sea Level Rise in Miami Dade County. https://www.arcgis.com/apps/Cascade/index.html?appid=6ff1c86445114dc7b82e13b67b439093

110   "NOAA Tides and Currents." NOAA Tides and Currents, 2022. https://tidesandcurrents.noaa.gov/ https://tidesandcurrents.noaa.gov/sltrends/sltrends_global_station.shtml?stnid=930-031

111   Miami Herald, Mike Lafferty 2/15/19 Internet

112   Google Scholar Profile of Shimon Wdowinski. http://scholar.google.com/citations?user=xWyN2wkAAAAJ&hl=en

113   National Geographic Society Newsroom – Ideas and Insight From National Geographic. "National Geographic Society Newsroom," November 16, 2022. https://blog.nationalgeographic.org

114   https://www.cleveland.com/weather/blog/2017/08/how_is_climate_change_affectin.html

115   National Geographic Society Newsroom – Ideas and Insight From National Geographic. "National Geographic Society Newsroom," November 16, 2022. https://blog.nationalgeographic.org

116   https://www.cleveland.com/weather/blog/2017/08/how_is_climate_change_affectin.html

117   https://www.chicagotribune.com/news/environment/ct-lake-michigan-water-levels-january-record-20200205 24afriu5fbltdg4mrbs5v4tvm-story.html

118   Eng, Monica. "Climate Change Is Already Impacting Lake Michigan — Here's How." NPR.org, September 16, 2019. https://www.npr.org/local/309/2019/09/16/760909053/climate-change-is-already-impacting-lake-michigan-here-s-how

119   Report lays out climate's treat to US security: NY Times 10/22/21

120   Ibid.

121   Climate Change 2021: The Physical Science Basis | Climate Change 2021: The Physical Science Basis. "Climate Change 2021: The Physical Science Basis." 2021. https://www.ipcc.ch/report/ar6/wg1/

122   Ibid.

123   This chart represents an approximation of sea level rise based upon the author's understanding of the UN IPCC writing. If there is a more accurate chart, the author would like to insert it in the next edition.

124   Adam, James, ed. *The Republic of Plato: Books VI-X and Indexes*. Vol. 2. at the University Press, 1902. The Republic by Plato, Book VII. pp. 514-521.

125   See Sparknotes.com

126   Email 11/12/21 to academic UN IPCC leader

127   This Is How Much Sea-Level Rise in These Cities Will Cost Taxpayers - TheStreet

128   NYC mayor has a $10 billion plan to protect Manhattan from rising seas - The Verge

129   IPCC Climate Change Report: UN Climate Change Panel's Damning Report: Code Red For Humanity (ndtv.com)

130   A $26 Billion Plan to Save the Houston Area From Rising Seas | WIRED

131   Julienne Stroeve, at the University of Manitoba, Canada

132   NASA Sea Level Change Portal. "Home." 2022. https://sealevel.nasa.gov/

133   CFACT letter 5/24/21 p. 5

134   Wrightstone, Gregory. *Inconvenient Facts: The Science that Al Gore Doesn't Want You to Know*. Silver Crown Productions, LLC, 2017. p. 80.

135   CFACT 5/24/2021 pg. 5

136   148 ships stranded in Arctic off Russia due to unexpected freeze. "18 Ships Stranded in Arctic off Russia Due to Unexpected Freeze," November 30, 2021. https://freerepublic.com/focus/f-news/4016839/posts

137   Viñas, Maria-José. "Study: Mass Gains of Antarctic Ice Sheet Greater than Losses – Climate Change: Vital Signs of the Planet." Climate Change: Vital Signs of the Planet, November 5, 2015. https://climate.nasa.gov/news/2361/study-mass-gains-of-antarctic-ice-sheet-greater-than-losses.
      NASA. "Space Laser Missions Map 16 Years of Ice Sheet Loss." 2020. http://www.nasa.gov/feature/goddard/2020/nasa-space-laser-missions-map-16-years-of-ice-sheet-loss

138   Vizcarra, Natasha. "Unexpected Ice | Earthdata." Earthdata, April 22, 2014. http://www.earthdata.nasa.gov/learn/sensing-our-planet/unexpected-ice

139   Principia Scientific Intl. | A science-based community. "Climate Shock: 90 Percent of the World's Glaciers Are GROWING | Principia Scientific Intl.," November 26, 2016. https://principia-scientific.com/climate-shock-90-percent-worlds-glaciers-growing/

140   Comiso, Josefino C. "Variability and trends in Antarctic surface temperatures from in situ and satellite infrared measurements." *Journal of Climate* 13, no. 10 (2000): 1674-1696.
      Doran, John W. "Soil health and global sustainability: Translating science into practice." *Agriculture, ecosystems & environment* 88, no. 2 (2002): 119-127.

141   World of Change: Antarctic Sea Ice. "World of Change: Antarctic Sea Ice." https://Earthobservatory.nasa.gov/world-of-change/sea-ice-antarctic

142   Climate study estimates sea level rise could cost Florida $75.8 billion by 2040 | wtsp.com https://ntrs.nasa.gov/api/citations/20180004341/downloads/20180004341.pdf?attachment=true

143   Climate Change reconsidered IKI fossil Fuels, p. 226

144   Nace, Trevor. "Arctic Sea Ice Is Growing Faster Than Before, But There's A Catch." Forbes, December 10, 2018. https://www.forbes.com/sites/trevornace/2018/12/10/arctic-sea-ice-is-growing-faster-than-before-but-theres-a-catch/

145   Lord Christopher Monckton, private correspondence Jan 7, 2019.

146   Gore, Al. *An inconvenient truth: The crisis of global warming*, p. 109. See Note 20 for more information.

147   Koonin, Steven E. "Opinion | Greenland's Melting Ice Is No Cause for Climate-Change Panic." WSJ. https://www.wsj.com/articles/greenland-melting-ice-panic-sheets-global-warming-variance-seal-level-rise-climate-change-carbon-fossil-fuel-11645131739

148   Fountain, Henry, and Derek Watkins. "As Greenland Melts, Where's the Water Going? (Published 2017)." As Greenland Melts, Where's the Water Going? - The New York Times, December 5, 2017. https://www.nytimes.com/interactive/2017/12/05/climate/greenland-ice-melting.html

149   https://wattsupwiththat.com/2019/06/19/if-greenland-is-catastrophically-melting-how-do-activists-explain-nasas-growing-greenland-glacier/

150   Greenland Ice Sheet Today | Surface Melt Data presented by NSIDC. "Greenland Ice Sheet Today | Surface Melt Data Presented by NSIDC," November 10, 2022. http://nsidc.org/greenland-today/

151   Environment. "A Greenland Glacier Is Growing. That's Not Good News," March 25, 2019. https://www.nationalgeographic.com/environment/article/one-part-of-greenland-ice-growing

152   Nature. "Mass Balance of the Greenland Ice Sheet from 1992 to 2018 - Nature," December 10, 2019. https://www.nature.com/articles/s41586-019-1855-2

CHAPTER 3

153   Watts Up With That? "What You Need to Know and Are Not Told about Hurricanes," September 15, 2017. https://wattsupwiththat.com/2017/09/15/what-you-need-to-know-and-are-not-told-about-hurricanes/

154   National Oceanic and Atmospheric Administration, a branch of the U.S. Government.

155   Watts Up With That? "What You Need to Know and Are Not Told about Hurricanes," September 15, 2017. https://wattsupwiththat.com/2017/09/15/what-you-need-to-know-and-are-not-told-about-hurricanes/

156   Watts Up With That? "The Washington Post's Slander on Hurricanes and Climate Change," September 16, 2018. https://wattsupwiththat.com/2018/09/16/the-washington-posts-slander-on-hurricanes-and-climate-change/

157   Wrightstone, Gregory. *Inconvenient Facts: The Science that Al Gore Doesn't Want You to Know*. Silver Crown Productions, LLC, 2017, p. 97.

158   World Wildlife Fund. "Why Are Glaciers and Sea Ice Melting?" 2022. https://www.worldwildlife.org/pages/why-are-glaciers-and-sea-ice-melting

159   "Climate Goalpost Migration: If You Can't Prove More Hurricanes, Say It's Making Them Relocate." Watts Up With That?, May 5, 2020. https://wattsupwiththat.com/2020/05/05/climate-goalpost-migration-if-you-cant-prove-more-hurricanes-say-its-making-them-relocate/

160   New York Post. "No, Global Warming Isn't Causing Worse Hurricanes," September 19, 2018. https://ny-post.com/2018/09/19/no-global-warming-isnt-causing-worse-hurricanes/

161   Marc Morano, Climate Change, p. 192

162   US EPA. "Climate Change Indicators: Tropical Cyclone Activity | US EPA," June 27, 2016. https://www.epa.gov/climate-indicators/climate-change-indicators-tropical-cyclone-activity

163   (Maui 2016 and Michaels 2015)

164   Because of the total control that the Climate Activists have over the media, you will not easily find articles which explain that there has been no increase in the number of hurricanes during recent history.

165   New York Post. "No, Global Warming Isn't Causing Worse Hurricanes," September 19, 2018. https://ny-post.com/2018/09/19/no-global-warming-isnt-causing-worse-hurricanes/
        Marc Morano, Climate Change, pg. 192

US EPA. "Climate Change Indicators: Tropical Cyclone Activity | US EPA," June 27, 2016. https://www. epa.gov/climate-indicators/climate-change-indicators-tropical-cyclone-activity

(Maui 2016 and Michaels 2015)

166   Watts Up With That? "What You Need to Know and Are Not Told about Hurricanes," September 15, 2017. https://wattsupwiththat.com/2017/09/15/what-you-need-to-know-and-are-not-told-about-hurricanes/

167   Watts Up With That? "The Washington Post's Slander on Hurricanes and Climate Change," September 16, 2018. https://wattsupwiththat.com/2018/09/16/the-washington-posts-slander-on-hurricanes-and-climate-change/
Watts Up With That? "Tropical Crime and Punishment," February 12, 2013. https://wattsupwiththat.com/2013/02/11/tropical-crime-and-punishment/

168   Global Tropical Cyclone Activity | Ryan Maue (climatlas.com)

169   **Florida State University. "Climate change altering frequency, intensity of hurricanes." 2015.** https://www.sciencedaily.com/releases/2015/05/150518121358.htm

170   Search on hurricane speeds. https://www.google.com/search?q=what+is+the+speed+of+a+category+four+hurricane&ie=UTF-8&oe=UTF-8&hl=en-us&client=safari

171   Watts Up With That? "The Washington Post's Slander on Hurricanes and Climate Change," September 16, 2018. https://wattsupwiththat.com/2018/09/16/the-washington-posts-slander-on-hurricanes-and-climate-change/
Watts Up With That? "Tropical Crime and Punishment," February 12, 2013. https://wattsupwiththat.com/2013/02/11/tropical-crime-and-punishment/

172   Global Monitoring Laboratory. Monthly Average Mauna Loa CO2. https://gml.noaa.gov/ccgg/trends/

173   Adler, Ben. "Climate Change Will Bring More Hurricanes to New York, Other Midlatitude Cities, Study Finds." Climate change will bring more hurricanes to New York, other midlatitude cities, study finds, 2022. https://news.yahoo.com/climate-change-will-bring-more-hurricanes-to-new-york-other-mid-latitude-cities-study-finds-184919327.html

174   Ibid

175   Ibid.

176   Search for hurricanes. https://en.wikipedia.org/wiki/List_of_New_York_hurricanes

177   Wrightstone, Gregory. *Inconvenient Facts: The Science that Al Gore Doesn't Want You to Know*. Silver Crown Productions, LLC, 2017, p. 92.

178   Smosaka, S. "No, We Can't Blame Tornadoes on Climate Change ... Yet." Grist, March 5, 2020. https://grist.org/climate/no-we-cant-blame-tornadoes-on-climate-change-yet/

179   Watts Up With That? "2018 U.S. Tornadoes on Track to Be Lowest Ever – NOAA's Temperature Trends Blow a Hole in 'Climate Correlation,'" October 24, 2018. https://wattsupwiththat.com/2018/10/24/2018-u-s-tornadoes-on-track-to-be-lowest-ever-noaas-temperature-trends-blow-a-hole-in-climate-correlation/

180   Doswell, Charles A., Alan R. Moller, and Harold E. Brooks. "Storm spotting and public awareness since the first tornado forecasts of 1948." *Weather and forecasting* 14, no. 4 (1999): 544-557.

181   Perry, Mark. "Inconvenient Weather Fact for Earth Day: The Frequency of Violent Tornadoes Fell to a Record Low in 2018." American Enterprise Institute - AEI, April 22, 2019. https://www.aei.org/carpe-diem/inconvenient-weather-fact-for-earth-day-the-frequency-of-violent-tornadoes-fell-to-a-record-low-in-2018/

182   US EPA. "Climate Change Indicators: Wildfires | US EPA," July 1, 2016. https://www.epa.gov/climate-indicators/climate-change-indicators-wildfires

183   Ibid.

184   Wrightstone, Gregory. *Inconvenient Facts: The Science that Al Gore Doesn't Want You to Know*. Silver Crown Productions, LLC, 2017, p. 111.

185   The Economist 8/26/2020

186   En.wikipedia.org

187   La Voce di New York. "California Under Fire: Jon Keeley Explains the State's Deadliest-Ever Wildfires," November 13, 2018. https://lavocedinewyork.com/en/news/2018/11/13/california-under-fire-jon-keeley-explains-the-states-deadliest-ever-wildfires/

188   La Voce di New York. "California Under Fire: Jon Keeley Explains the State's Deadliest-
       Ever Wildfires," November 13, 2018. https://lavocedinewyork.com/en/news/2018/11/13/
       california-under-fire-jon-keeley-explains-the-states-deadliest-ever-wildfires/

189   Facts + Statistics: Wildfires | III. "Facts + Statistics: Wildfires | III." 2022. https://www.iii.org/fact-statistic/
       facts-statistics-wildfires

190   Between 2000 and 2020, there have been a half-million acres burned due to powerline-ignited fires, which is
       five times greater than the previous 20 years.

191   Shellenberger, Michael. "Why Everything They Say About California Fires
       — Including That Climate Matters Most — Is Wrong." Forbes, November
       4, 2019. https://www.forbes.com/sites/michaelshellenberger/2019/11/04/
       why-everything-they-say-about-california-fires--including-that-climate-matters-most--is-wrong/

192   Between 2000 and 2020, there have been a half-million acres burned due to powerline-ignited fires, which is
       five times greater than the previous 20 years

193   See Note 193 for more information. https://www.forbes.com/sites/michaelshellenberger/2019/11/04/why-
       everything-they-say-about-california-fires--including-that-climate-matters-most--is-wrong/#278b49fa4cb6

194   https://www.fs.fed.us/psw/publications/mckelvey/mckelvey3.pdf

195   Western Watersheds Project. "Why Thinning Forests Is Poor Wildfire Strategy - Western Watersheds
       Project," November 17, 2022. https://www.westernwatersheds.org/gw-poor-wildfire-strategy/

196   A famous English clergyman and poet who lived 400 year ago.

197   In other words, WE are the cause of most forest fires, so don't blame GW.

198   In. Wikipedia.org

199   WMO Weather and Climate Extreme.News.un.org 8/18/20 Climate Change. Actually, the warmest day in
       Death Valley was 134°F on July 10, 1913

200   NPS.gov

201   "Global Climate in 2015-2019: Climate Change Accelerates." World Meteorological
       Organization, September 24, 2019. https://public.wmo.int/en/media/press-release/
       global-climate-2015-2019-climate-change-accelerates

202   Google search for average temperatures in Alaska. https://www.google.com/search?q=nome+alaska+averag
       e+temperature+in+january&ie=UTF-8&oe=UTF-8&hl=en-us&client=safari

203   (Christy 2015). (Heatwave EPA 2016b)

204   Wrightstone, Gregory. Inconvenient Facts: The Science that Al Gore Doesn't Want You to Know. Silver Crown
       Productions, LLC, 2017, p. 82.

205   Koonicn, Steven. "A deceptive Report on Climate," Wall Street Journal, 3/11/2017, p. A15.

206   Wrightstone, Gregory. Inconvenient Facts: The Science that Al Gore Doesn't Want You to Know. Silver Crown
       Productions, LLC, 2017, p. 82.

207   Climate Change: Vital Signs of the Planet. "Earth's Freshwater Future: Extremes of Flood and
       Drought – Climate Change: Vital Signs of the Planet." 2022. https://climate.nasa.gov/news/2881/
       earths-freshwater-future-extremes-of-flood-and-drought

208   Marc Morano, Climate Change, p. 102.

209   Competitive Enterprise Institute. "Wrong Again: 50 Years of Failed Eco-Pocalyptic
       Predictions - Competitive Enterprise Institute," September 18, 2019. https://cei.org/blog/
       wrong-again-50-years-of-failed-eco-pocalyptic-predictions/

210   (The EPA Palmer drought-severity index and the NOAA 2017a charts)

211   Marc Morano, Climate Change, p. 102.

212   (Examples: 1930 U.S. Dust Bowl and 1960s African Sahel)

213   The Max Planck Institute; de Jong 2013 and Zhu 2016. See Wrightstone, Gregory. Inconvenient Facts: The
       Science that Al Gore Doesn't Want You to Know. Silver Crown Productions, LLC, 2017, pp. 66-68.

214   U.S. Percentage Areas (Very Warm/Cold, Very Wet/Dry) | National Centers for Environmental
       Information (NCEI). "U.S. Percentage Areas (Very Warm/Cold, Very Wet/Dry) | National Centers for
       Environmental Information (NCEI)." https://www.ncdc.noaa.gov/temp-and-precip/uspa/wet-dry/12

215   Associated Press, June 30, 1989.Quoted in Lukewarming. by Michaels and Knappenberger, p. 179. See Note 53 for source information.

216   McCabe and Wolock, "Spatial and Temporal Patterns in Coterminous US streamflow characteristics," Geophysical Research letters, 41 (2014); 6889-97. Quoted from p. 180 in Lukewarming, cited above.

217   Search for listing of floods. https://en.wikipedia.org/wiki/List_of_floods

218   Mississippi flood 1927 - Bing

219   Picture from President Coolidge's autobiography (no page number listed)

220   Search for floods in China. https://en.wikipedia.org/wiki/2020_China_floods

221   By Chinese tradition and mythology this occurred in 2300 BC.

222   Search for flood information in China. https://en.wikipedia.org/wiki/Great_Flood_(China)

223   Search for flood information. https://en.wikipedia.org/wiki/2020_Jakarta_floods

224   Espinel, Zelde, James P. Kossin, Sandro Galea, Anne S. Richardson, and James M. Shultz. "Forecast: increasing mental health consequences from Atlantic hurricanes throughout the 21st century." *Psychiatric services* 70, no. 12 (2019): 1165-1167. https://ps.psychiatryonline.org/doi/10.1176/appi.ps.201900273

225   "Climate Change Reconsidered II: Fossil Fuels,"p. 202. See Note 4 for source information.

226   Ibid.

227   Merriam Webster dictionary

228   Ibid.

229   Quotation search. https://www.quotes.net/mquote/65686

230   Quotation search. https://www.quotes.net/mquote/65711

CHAPTER 4

231   USA TODAY. "One-Third of All Plant and Animal Species Could Be Extinct in 50 Years, Study Warns." 2020. https://www.usatoday.com/story/news/nation/2020/02/14/climate-change-study-plant-animal-extinction/4760646002/

232   U.N. report: 1 million species of animals and plants face extinction due to climate change and human activity - CBS News

233   Humans are driving one million species to extinction (nature.com). "The (U,N.) report draws inextricable links between biodiversity loss and climate change. An estimated 5% of all species would be threatened with extinction by 2 °C of warming above pre-industrial levels — a threshold that the world could breach in the next few decades, unless greenhouse-gas emissions are drastically reduced. Earth could lose 16% of its species if the average global temperature rise exceeds 4.3 °C. Such damage to ecosystems would undermine global efforts to reduce poverty and hunger and promote more-sustainable development, the IPBES report says."

234   Climate change and biodiversity loss should be tackled together | Research and Innovation (europa.eu)

235   4 Catastrophic Climate Predictions That Never Came True - Foundation for Economic Education. "4 Catastrophic Climate Predictions That Never Came True | Laura Williams," September 5, 2019. https://fee.org/articles/4-catastrophic-climate-predictions-that-never-came-true/

236   Mass Extinction Lie Exposed: Life is Thriving | The Freedom Pub. "Mass Extinction Lie Exposed: Life Is Thriving | The Freedom Pub," January 21, 2019. https://blog.heartland.org/2019/05/mass-extinction-lie-exposed-life-is-thriving/

237   Also, a substantial donation which would make you "part of the solution and protect the planet" and would be appreciated.

238   www.world wildlife.org. For additional confirmation, virtually every Climate Activist supporting organization agrees that we must save the polar bear from CC including polarbearinternational.org, the American Museum of Natural History and www.biodiversity.org,

239   Gore, Al. *An inconvenient truth: The crisis of global warming*, p. 146. See Note 20 for more information.

240   Polar Bear Science. "Challenging NOAA's 'Arctic Report Card 2014' on Polar Bears," December 19, 2014. https://polarbearscience.com/2014/12/19/challenging-noaas-arctic-report-card-2014-on-polar-bears/

241   Video. "Polar Bear Scare Unmasked: The Saga of a Toppled Global Warming Icon." https://www.youtube. com/watch?v=z6bcCTFnGZ0

242   See "the slaughter of polar bears that rarely gets mentioned" in polarbearscience.com 9/20/2012. https:// polarbearscience.com/2012/09/20/the-slaughter-of-polar-bears-that-rarely-gets-mentioned-ca-1890-1930/

243   UPI. "Poaching Threatens Russian Polar Bears," March 22, 2013. https://www.upi.com/Science_ News/2013/03/22/Poaching-threatens-Russian-polar-bears/32241363990554/
Search on conservation and protection of polar bears. https://en.wikipedia.org/wiki/ Agreement_on_the_Conservation_of_Polar_Bears

244   Fur Institute of Canada. "Polar Bear Population and Management." https://fur.ca/conservation/ the-polar-bear-debate/

245   Yale E360. "As Polar Bear Attacks Increase in Warming Arctic, a Search for Solutions." https://e360.yale. edu/features/as-polar-bear-attacks-increase-in-warming-arctic-a-search-for-solutions

246   350+ Polar bear Pictures | Download Free Images on Unsplash

247   See "the slaughter of Polar bears that rarely gets mentioned" in polarbearscience.com 9/20/2012

248   An Exchange of Research and Culture – Dr. Dorthe Dahl-Jensen | Center for Remote Sensing of Ice Sheets (ku.edu)

249   Michaels, Patrick. "Save the Polar Bears? They're Fine, Actually." Cato Institute, 2016. https://www.cato. org/publications/commentary/save-polar-bears-theyre-fine-actually
Video. "The Only Man In The World Who Can Swim With A Polar Bear: Grizzly Man." https://www. youtube.com/watch?v=g7rZTZBOrqQ

250   Susan Crockford Responds To BBC's "Misleading" Article on Polar Bears | NOT A LOT OF PEOPLE KNOW THAT (wordpress.com)

251   Video. "Polar Bear Hearing: Armstrong Testimony." https://www.youtube.com/watch?v=-Yr5HxJTQAw

252   Lehr, Jay. "Polar Bears: The End of a Climate Delusion Icon - CFACT." CFACT, January 22, 2020. https:// www.cfact.org/2020/01/22/polar-bears-the-end-of-a-climate-delusion-icon/

253   At least no one is currently burned at the stake for stating an opinion contrary to Climate Activist beliefs.

254   Undisclosed Organization. Call me if you want to know its name.

255   Video. Crockford, Susan. "The Polar Bear Catastrophe That Never Happened." https://www.youtube.com/ watch?v=8VwzUBc1rsc

256   Information on Susan Crockford. https://en.wikipedia.org/wiki/Susan_J._Crockford

257   Chapter 10 of The Polar Bear Catastrophe That Never Happened (Dr. Susan Crockford 2019).

258   Ibid.

259   Virtual Caribbean Dive: "Virtual Caribbean Dive:" http://www.virtualcoralreefdive.com/

260   Ibid.

261   Ocean service. NOAA.gov

262   As you would expect, NOAA computers project another 0.3 to 0.4 pH units by 2100", about four times the real current rate.ge.

263   Rapier, Robert. "No, The Oceans Are Not Acidic." Forbes, February 1, 2020. https://www.forbes.com/sites/ rrapier/2020/02/01/no-the-oceans-are-not-acidic/

264   Ocean acidification | National Oceanic and Atmospheric Administration. "Ocean Acidification," April 1, 2020. https://www.noaa.gov/education/resource-collections/ocean-coasts/ocean-acidification

265   https://content.sciendo.com/view/journals/quageo/38/3/article-p59.xml?language=en

266   NOAA (Ocean Acidification)

267   Watts Up With That? "Ocean pH Accuracy Arguments Challenged with 80 Years of Instrumental Data," March 31, 2015. https://wattsupwiththat.com/2015/03/31/ ocean-ph-accuracy-arguments-challenged-with-80-years-of-instrumental-data/

268   UNESCO. "Ocean Acidification," November 19, 2018. https://en.unesco.org/ocean-acidification

269   Forbes Trevor Nace 2/24/2020

270   Woods Hole Oceanographic Institution
      What is coral bleaching? "What Is Coral Bleaching?" https://oceanservice.noaa.gov/facts/coral_bleach.html
      Kamenos, Nicholas, and Sebastian Hennige. "The Great Barrier Reef Has Been Bleaching for at Least
      400 Years, but It's Getting Worse." The Conversation, August 16, 2018. http://theconversation.com/
      the-great-barrier-reef-has-been-bleaching-for-at-least-400-years-but-its-getting-worse-101691

271   Watts Up With That? "Ocean pH Accuracy Arguments Challenged with 80 Years
      of Instrumental Data," March 31, 2015. https://wattsupwiththat.com/2015/03/31/
      ocean-ph-accuracy-arguments-challenged-with-80-years-of-instrumental-data/

272   UNESCO. "Ocean Acidification," November 19, 2018. https://en.unesco.org/ocean-acidification

273   ABC Science. "Crown of Thorns Starfish | Coral reef killers." https://www.youtube.com/
      watch?v=-tG60zUFW-A

274   Search for information on corals. Wikipedia, corals.

275   David Grimes, Good Thinking, p. 311. Grimes points out that the burden of scientific proof is on the person
      who makes the claim, not the person who disputes the claim.

276   Vuckovic, Djordje, Amanda I. Tinoco, Lorraine Ling, Christian Renicke, John R. Pringle, and William A.
      Mitch. "Conversion of oxybenzone sunscreen to phototoxic glucoside conjugates by sea anemones and cor-
      als." Science 376, no. 6593 (2022): 644-648. https://www.science.org/doi/10.1126/science.abn2600

277   Rosenberg Martha. Epoch Times, April 27-Muy 3. 2022, p. C3.

278   NY Times

279   Colorescience. "Where Is Sunscreen Banned? 4 Countries with Bans on Sunscreen," May 11, 2020. https://
      www.colorescience.com/blogs/blog/sunscreen-bans

280   Wikipedia

281   Cornell University study

282   https://reefnation.com/can-coral-reefs-adapt-to-low-ph-conditions/

283   Ho, Leonard. "Lower pH Found to Slow Bacterial Coral Disease." Reefs.com, June 19, 2017. https://reefs.
      com/lower-ph-found-to-slow-bacterial-coral-disease/

284   Mongabay News, March 3, 2020.

285   Ibid.

286   Hoffner, Erik. "Conservation Nation: How Palau Protects Its Reefs and Waters (Commentary)."
      Mongabay Environmental News, March 6, 2020. https://news.mongabay.com/2020/03/
      conservation-nation-how-palau-protects-its-reefs-and-waters-commentary/

287   Ibid.

288   NOAA U.S. Government

289   The average water temperature at the Great Barrier Reef is 27°C. and Australia is closer to the South Pole.

290   Ibid.

291   Climate Activists, please check this one out. It contradicts your basic thesis.

292   Although the authors report "It is getting worse," they provide no evidence of that. It is quite probable that
      they would have had difficulty getting approval for this article if they had not written "It is getting worse."
      Kamenos, Nicholas, and Sebastian Hennige. "The Great Barrier Reef Has Been Bleaching for at Least
      400 Years, but It's Getting Worse." The Conversation, August 16, 2018. http://theconversation.com/
      the-great-barrier-reef-has-been-bleaching-for-at-least-400-years-but-its-getting-worse-101691

293   Sear on tourism and reefs. Tourism on the Great Barrier Reef - Wikipedia. https://en.wikipedia.org/wiki/
      Tourism_on_the_Great_Barrier_Reef

294   See Tech by Vice, Wendy Syfret 12/17/2015 and Vice Magazine 12/15. Also see the 2016 study in the
      Archives of Environments have discovered that the chemicals commonly found in sunscreen are contribut-
      ing - in large measure - to the problem (Bleaching, Contamination and Toxicology described in Good
      Nature Travel by Candice Gaukel Andrews 7/23/2019 which states "scientist at the Great Barrier Reef").

295   Ibid.

296   James Cook University. News Release 4/2018. Jcu.edu.au

297   Coral Reefs in the Kimberley Adapt to Survive | The Pew Charitable Trusts. "Coral Reefs in the Kimberley Adapt to Survive," November 20, 2020. https://www.pewtrusts.org/en/research-and-analysis/reports/2020/11/coral-reefs-in-the-kimberley-adapt-to-survive

298   Readfearn, Graham. "Rowley Shoals: Thriving Australian Reef Shows What's Possible When Ecosystems Are Untouched by Humans." the Guardian, April 7, 2021. http://www.theguardian.com/environment/2021/apr/07/rowley-shoals-thriving-australian-reef-shows-whats-possible-when-ecosystems-are-untouched-by-humans

299   The effects of ultraviolet filters and sunscreen on corals and aquatic ecosystems. "The Effects of Ultraviolet Filters and Sunscreen on Corals and Aquatic Ecosystems." https://www.coris.noaa.gov/activities/effects-ultraviolet-filters-sunscreen-corals/welcome.html
       Natural Threats to Coral Reefs: Corals Tutorial. "Natural Threats to Coral Reefs: Corals Tutorial." https://oceanservice.noaa.gov/education/tutorial_corals/coral08_naturalthreats.htm

300   Search on dodo birds. https://www.google.com/search?q=Why+did+the+dodo+bird+become+extinct&ie=UTF-8&oe=UTF-8&hl=en-uclient=safari

301   Extinct thinking: was the hapless dodo really destined to die out? | Science | The Guardian.

302   Search for animals that have recently gone extinct. https://www.google.com/search?client=safari&hl=en-us&sxsrf=ALeKk03uwwSGAGZ_GIsssQGh-9TKIHTHpA:1615547596781&q=Animals+recently+extinct&stick=H4sIAAAAAAAAAOOQMZJIzMvMTcwpVihKTU7NK8mpVEitKMnMSy6JMoPJQAUU0orycxXSc_KTEnMUyhOLcjPz0hUS81IUknOA6kpSFZIzEvPSU08xcunn6hsYlRVnG5meYuQEcUzNcquSTjFygCWSigqhTPMMgyIo07QqpxzKTE8zMIPqM8zOKjeFCptZ5hZBhc2KjeKNYPaYWVSUZ_1ilHDE4Y8GFsZFrDhlb7FJMmhNreJilkqsi3d3rrDh6voUuNKau-ynjjoAsdj2yx4BAAA&sa=X&ved=2ahUKEwjTpv7kz6rvAhVKXM0KHRnnDsgQ4qYDMA96BAgYEAk&biw=833&bih=593&dpr=2

303   Dodo bird extinct - Google Search .https://www.britannica.com/animal/dodo-nctexti-bird

304   Meijer, Hanneke. "Extinct Thinking: Was the Hapless Dodo Really Destined to Die Out?" the Guardian, December 2, 2015. http://www.theguardian.com/science/blog/2015/dec/02/extinct-thinking-was-the-hapless-dodo-really-destined-to-die-out

305   Search for animals that have gone extinct due to global warming. https://www.google.com/search-?q=What+animals+became+extinct+due+to+global+warming&ie=UTF-8&oe=UTF-8&hl=en-us&client=safari

306   Search for animals that have gone extinct due to global warming. https://www.google.com/search-?q=What+animals+became+extinct+due+to+global+warming&ie=UTF-8&oe=UTF-8&hl=en-us&client=safari

307   Co2nsensus. "Co2nsensus." https://www.co2nsensus.com/blog/animals-that-have-gone-extinct-due-to-global-warming

308   Also listed was the Golden Toad which was extinct.

309   Golden toad extinct - Google Search. https://www.google.com/search?q=golden+toad+extinct&ie=UTF-8&oe=UTF-8&hl=en-us&client=safari

310   AAAS. "Science | AAAS." https://www.sciencemag.org/news/2010/03/global-warming-didnt-kill-golden-toad

311   Sader, Steven A., and Armond T. Joyce. "Deforestation rates and trends in Costa Rica, 1940 to 1983." *Biotropica* (1988): 11-19. https://jstor.org/stable/2388421?seq=1

312   Costa Rica - Climatology | Climate Change Knowledge Portal. "World Bank Climate Change Knowledge Portal." https://climateknowledgeportal.worldbank.org/
       Image from US Fish and Wildlife Service

313   Sader, Steven A., and Armond T. Joyce. "Deforestation rates and trends in Costa Rica, 1940 to 1983." *Biotropica* (1988): 11-19. https://jstor.org/stable/2388421?seq=1

314   Costa Rica - Climatology | Climate Change Knowledge Portal. "World Bank Climate Change Knowledge Portal." https://climateknowledgeportal.worldbank.org/
       Image from US Fish and Wildlife Service

315   See Polar bear section above.

316   WWF. "Adélie Penguin: Antarctic Birds with Attitude." https://www.wwf.org.uk/learn/wildlife/adelie-penguins

317   Atlantic Cod | FishWatch. "Atlantic Cod FishWatch," February 17, 2022. "Atlantic Cod: The good, the bad, and the rebuilding - Part 1. https://www.fishwatch.gov/profiles/atlantic-cod

318   See Note 319

319   NOAA. "Staghorn Coral," August 5, 2022. https://www.fisheries.noaa.gov/species/staghorn-coral

320   Ibid.

321   Orangespotted Filefish, Harlequin Filefish - Oxymonacanthus longirostris. "Orangespotted Filefish, Harlequin Filefish - Oxymonacanthus Longirostris." https://www.bluezooaquatics.com/productDetail.asp?did=1&pid=532&cid=282

322   There are many claims that some animals have become extinct, most of which almost no one has heard of and none for which I have seen any scientific proof. My request is that if the reader finds scientific proof of such an event, that the readers contact the author who will provide a free signed copy of this book to that reader.

323   Bird identification and information. https://identify.whatbird.com/obj/292/overview/Greater_White-fronted_Goose.aspx

324   Photos of White Fronted Goose. White fronted goose photos - Bing. https://www.bing.com/search?q=white+fronted+goose+photos&cvid=901ea8ad4a46423397af07bbd6fca083&pglt=547&FORM=ANSPA1&PC=HCTS

325   Search on White Fronted Goose. https://en.wikipedia.org/wiki/Greater_white-fronted_goose

326   Bird guide information on Greater White Fronted Goose. https://www.allaboutbirds.org/guide/Greater_White-fronted_Goose/id

327   Animal facts and information on Glass Frogs. https://animalsake.com/interesting-facts-about-glass-frogs

328   Wikipedia

329   Search for photos of glass frogs. 1,471 Glass Frog Photos - Free & Royalty-Free Stock Photos from Dreamstime. https://www.dreamstime.com/photos-images/glass-frog.html

330   Animals. "Mouse Lemurs | National Geographic." Ahttps://www.nationalgeographic.com/animals/mammals/facts/mouse-lemurs

331   Search for information on dwarf lemurs. Greater dwarf lemur - Wikipedia. Animals. "Mouse Lemurs | National Geographic." https://www.nationalgeographic.com/animals/mammals/facts/mouse-lemurs

332   Center for Biological Diversity. "Center for Biological Diversity." https://biologicaldiversity.org

333   Macaroni Penguin Facts - Photos - Earth's Endangered Creatures. "Macaroni Penguin Facts - Photos - Earth's Endangered Creatures." http://www.earthsendangered.com/profile.asp?sp=14683

334   Search for information on the coqui tree frog. https://search.yahoo.com/yhs/search?hspart=pty&hsimp=yhs-pty_email&param2=7e27520d-df80-40fa-9272-9f5a926a18f0&param3=email_~US~appfocus1-&param4=d-ccc9-lp0-cp_6449165025ilc-bb9-iei-yho~MSIE~coqui+tree+frong-D41D8CD98F00B204E9800998ECF8427E~Win7&param1=20191202&us_privacy=1---&p=coqui+tree+frong&type=em_appfocus1_ie.

335   Department of Land and Natural Resources. "Department of Land and Natural Resources." https://dlnr.hawaii.gov

336   Search for photos of coqui frogs. 38 Coqui Frog Stock Photos, Pictures & Royalty-Free Images - iStock (istockphoto.com). https://www.istockphoto.com/photos/coqui-frog

337   Search for images of fur seals. https://images.search.yahoo.com/yhs/search?p=antarctic+fur+seal&fr=yhs-pty-pty_email&hspart=pty&hsimp=yhs-pty_email&imgurl=https%3A%2F%2Fwww.coolantarctica.com%2FAntarctica%2520fact%2520file%2Fwildlife%2Fsolo17.jpg.#id=4&iurl=https%3A%2F%2Fwww.coolantarctica.com%2FAntarctica%2520fact%2520file%2Fwildlife%2Fsolo17.jpg.&action=click

338   Wikipedia

339   Search for information on Wattled Crane. https://en.wikipedia.org/wiki/Wattled_crane

340   Search for facts and information on the wattled crane. http://animalia.bio/wattled-crane

341   Search for information on wattled crane. Wattled crane - Wikipedia. https://en.wikipedia.org/wiki/Wattled_crane

342   BioExpedition. "Yellow Eyed Penguin." BioExpedition, November 13, 2012. https://www.bioexpedition. com/yellow-eyed-penguin/

343   Search for information on yellow-eyed penguin. https://en.wikipedia.org/wiki/Yellow-eyed_penguin

344   Search for information on yellow eyed penguin - Google Search. https://www.google.com/search?as_ st=y&tbm=isch&hl=en-US&as_q=yellow+eyed+penguin&as_epq=&as_oq=&as_eq=&imgsz=&imgar=&img c=&imgcolor=&imgtype=&cr=&as_sitesearch=&safe=images&as_filetype=&tbs=#imgrc=ZxivE5QAUywO JM

345   Researchgate.net Department of Conservation. Wellington NZ. January 2012.

346   Ncbi.nim.nih.gov 5/16/2017 J Peer.

347   The Guardian. "Fears for World's Rarest Penguin as Population Plummets," November 27, 2017. http://www.theguardian.com/world/2017/nov/27/ population-worlds-rarest-penguins-plummets-yellow-eyed-new-zealand

348   Search for information on red breasted goose. https://en.wikipedia.org/wiki/Red-breasted_goose

349   Unep-aewa.org, Dr. Nicky Petkov.

350   Search for images of red breasted goose. 23 Red breasted goose ideas | goose, waterfowl, birds (pinterest. com). https://www.pinterest.com/btaxidermy/red-breasted-goose/

351   Search for information on red breasted goose. https://en.wikipedia.org/wiki/Red-breasted_goose

352   Red-breasted Goose (Branta ruficollis) - BirdLife species factsheet. "Red-Breasted Goose (Branta Ruficollis) - BirdLife Species Factsheet." http://datazone.birdlife.org/species/factsheet/22679954

353   Image search for grey headed albatross. Grey headed albatross - Yahoo Image Search Results. https://im- ages.search.yahoo.com/search/images?p=grey+headed+albatross&fr=yfp-t&imgurl=https%3A%2F%2Fi. pinimg.com%2Foriginals%2F46%2F14%2Fef%2F4614eff6cbfb1065f5521b3710ac6394. jpg#id=4&iurl=https%3A%2F%2Fi.pinimg.com%2Foriginals%2F46%2F14%2Fef%2F4614eff6cbfb1065f55 21b3710ac6394.jpg&action=click

354   Jref.com .komachi 5/26/12.

355   Jsonline.com 3/12/2021 p. 13a

356   "Bowhead Whale Facts, Pictures, Info: Discover A Long-Lived Arctic Whale." Active Wild, September 11, 2019. https://www.activewild.com/bowhead-whale/

357   Bowhead Whale - Whale Facts and Information. "Bowhead Whale - Whale Facts and Information." https://www.whale-world.com/bowhead-whale/

358   Bowhead whale. "Bowhead Whale." https://www.biologicaldiversity.org/species/mammals/bowhead_ whale/index.html

359   Whale & Dolphin Conservation USA. "Bowhead Whale." https://us.whales.org/whales-dolphins/ species-guide/bowhead-whale/

360   Search for images of bowhead whales. https://images.search.yahoo.com/yhs/search?p=bowhead+whale l+photos&fr=yhs-pty-pty_email&hspart=pty&hsimp=yhs-pty-email&imgurl=http%3A%2F%2Fimage. chinatopix.com%2Fdata%2Fimages%2Ffull%2F29585%2Fbowhead-whale.jpg.#id=14&iurl=http%3A%2F %2Fimage.chinatopix.com%2Fdata%2Fimages%2Ffull%2F29585%2Fbowhead-whale.jpg.&action=click

361   Search for photos of leopard seals. https://unsplash.com/s/photos/leopard-seal

362   Search for information on leopard seals. Leopard seal - Wikipedia. https://en.wikipedia.org/wiki/ Leopard_seal

363   Leopard seal – Australian Antarctic Program. "Leopard Seal," March 20, 2018. https://www.antarctica.gov. au/about-antarctica/animals/seals/leopard-seal/
Search for information on leopard seals. https://en.wikipedia.org/wiki/Leopard_seal

364   Search for photos of emperor penguins. https://unsplash.com/s/photos/emperor-penguin

365   Search for information on emperor penguins. https://en.wikipedia.org/wiki/Emperor_penguin

366   Climate Change: Satellites find new colonies of Emperor penguins BBC 8/5/20. Emperor penguin - Wikipedia Emperor Penguin (beauty-animal.blogspot.com). https://beauty-animal.blogspot.com/2011/12/ emperor-penguin.html

Search for information on emperor penguins. Emperor penguin - Wikipedia. https://en.wikipedia.org/wiki/Emperor_penguin

Emperor Penguin. "Emperor Penguin," December 8, 2011. http://beauty-animal.blogspot.com/2011/12/emperor-penguin.html

367   Search for information on emperor penguin extinction. https://search.yahoo.com/yhs/search?hspart=pty&hsimp=yhs-pty_email&param2=7e27520d-df80-40fa-9272-9f5a926a18f0&param3=email_~US~appfocus1~&param4=d-ccc9-lp0-cp_6449165025ilc-bb9-iei-yho~MSIE~emperor+penguin+extinction~D41D8CD98F00B204E9800998ECF8427E~Win7&param1=20191202&us_privacy=1---&p=emperor+penguin+extinction&type=em_appfocus1_ie
Articles on emperor penguins. https://www.nytimes.com/2019/04/25/science/emperor-penguins-antarctica.html

368   "Golden Toad Facts." http://extinct-animals-facts.com/Recently-Extinct-Animal-Facts/Golden-Toad-Facts.shtml

369   Golden Toad: The Animal Files. "Golden Toad: The Animal Files." http://www.theanimalfiles.com/amphibians/toads/golden_toad.html

370   In other words, "It is our fault" .from Julius Caesar by William Shakespeare. One of the major writings of Western Civilization.

CHAPTER 5

371   Michaels, Patrick J., and Paul C. Knappenberger. *Lukewarming: The new climate science that changes everything*. Cato Institute, 2016, p. 145.

372   You won't find any information on Ehrlich's support of global cooling here: https://en.wikipedia.org/wiki/Paul_R._Ehrlich

373   Friedan, Betty. "The Coming Ice Age." Harper's Magazine , May 9, 2019. https://harpers.org/archive/1958/09/the-coming-ice-age/

374   http://personal.psu.edu/lxv1/climate3.htmlKenneth Watt

375   Dr. Rasool of NASA in the Washington Post, 7/9/71

376   Ibid.

377   Wrightstone, Gregory. *Inconvenient Facts: The Science that Al Gore Doesn't Want You to Know*. Silver Crown Productions, LLC, 2017, p. 25.

378   HadCRUT4 Global Mean Temperature Change monthly data

379   Greta Thunberg is another major influencer who will be addressed in a later chapter.

380   Journal of Geophysical Research, Vol 93, pp. 9341-9364. August 20, 1988.

381   "A Look Back at James Hansen's Seminal Testimony on Climate, Part One." Grist, June 16, 2008. https://grist.org/article/a-climate-hero-the-early-years/

382   Fact letter 5/14/21 pg. 4

383   Skeptical Science. "Skeptical Science." https://www.skepticalscience.com/Hansen-1988-prediction.htm

384   Michaels, Pat , and Ryan Maue. "Thirty Years On, How Well Do Global Warming Predictions Stand Up?" WSJ. https://www.wsj.com/articles/thirty-years-on-how-well-do-global-warming-predictions-stand-up-1529623442

385   Data graph. https://www.sealevel.info/HADCRUT4_1988-2019_woodfortrees18.png

386   Data graph. https://www.sealevel.info/HADCRUT4_1988-2019_woodfortrees18.png

387   HadCRUT4 and UAH6 are internationally recognized groups that measure global temperatures.

388   The dark green line is Hansen's prediction, while the red line is the surface station record of global temperatures maintained by the British Met Office's Hadley Centre. The light green line is the Hadley Centre's estimate of the temperature trend from 1988 to 2020; the blue line is the temperature trend for the same period based on University of Alabama – Huntsville (UAH) satellite data.

389   Bloomberg - Are you a robot? "Bloomberg - Are You a Robot?" https://www.bloomberg.com/opinion/articles/2020-01-30/1988-global-warming-forecast-by-james-hansen-proved-mostly-true

390   His work was featured in Al Gore's book and movie, An Inconvenient Truth. Gore, Al. *An inconvenient truth: The crisis of global warming*. See Note 20 for more information.

391   Mann, Michael E., Raymond S. Bradley, and Malcolm K. Hughes. "Global-scale temperature patterns and climate forcing over the past six centuries." *Nature* 392, no. 6678 (1998): 779-787.

392   It should be pointed out that 2015-16 as shown in the previous graph was warmer than the chart above.

393   Wattsupwiththat.com

394   It should be pointed out that 2015-16 as shown in the previous graph was warmer than the chart above.

395   See Singer, Siegfried Fred. *Hot talk, cold science: Global warming's unfinished debate*. Independent Inst, 1999. Chapter 5.

396   Stephen McIntyre points out that "there was a fundamental inconsistency between the observed decline in tree ring widths and densities in the late 20th century… and temperature reconstructions from proxy networks dominated by tree rings. This was a scientific question. https://climateaudit.org/

397   NCEE Report. https://www.epa.gov/sites/default/files/2014-12/documents/incorporating_catastrophic_climate-change_into_policy_analysis.pdf

398   https://www.theguardian.com/environment/2016/aug/30/nasa-climate-change-warning-Earth-temperature-warming

399   "Climate Change Threatens the Survival of Coral Reefs Only 12 years to Avoid the Worst Damage." http://coralreefs.org/wp-content/uploads/2020/02/modified-consensus-statement-ICRS-2018.pdf

400   Climate catastrophe? A half a degree warming could make the difference I Science I AAAS

401   The climate disaster is here – this is what the future looks like I Environment I The Guardian

402   Prof. John Christy, the Distinguished Professor of Atmospheric Science and Director of the Earth System Science Center at The University of Alabama at Huntsville.

403   https://www.ieca-us.com/wp-content/uploads/John-Christy_Alabama-State-Climatologist-Comments_12.01.14.pd

404   Hourdin, Frédéric, Thorsten Mauritsen, Andrew Gettelman, Jean-Christophe Golaz, Venkatramani Balaji, Qingyun Duan, Doris Folini et al. "The art and science of climate model tuning." *Bulletin of the American Meteorological Society* 98, no. 3 (2017): 589-602.

405   Ibid.

406   Rohde, Robert. "Global Temperature Report for 2020 - Berkeley Earth." Berkeley Earth, January 14, 2021. http://berkeleyearth.org/global-temperature-report-for-2020/

407   WSJ 2/7/22, p. A9.

408   Environment and Climate News, 2/22, p. 22.

409   Ibid.

410   Ibid.

411   Associated Press, June 30, 1989. Quoted in Lukewarming by Michaels and Knappenberger, p. 179. See Note 53 for source information.

412   McDougall, Dan. "Sleeping in Fields, Eating Ice and Dirt." The Guardian. Guardian News and Media, October 11, 2005. https://www.theguardian.com/environment/2005/oct/12/naturaldisasters.climatechange

413   Sheffer, Lenton and Hayhoe, K. Milwaukee Journal Sentinel, p. 6A, 5/5/2020.

414   Ibid.

415   Hayhoe, Katharine. *"What's the Big Deal With a Few Degrees?"* YouTube, 2019. https://www.youtube.com/watch?v=6cRCbgTA_78

416   Search for population information on Burkina Faso. https://upload.wikimedia.org/wikipedia/commons/a/a1/Burkina_Faso_population.svg

417   "Global Climate in 2015-2019: Climate Change Accelerates." World Meteorological Organization, September 24, 2019. https://public.wmo.int/en/media/press-release/global-climate-2015-2019-climate-change-accelerates

418   Koonin, Steven E. "A Deceptive New Report on Climate." WSJ. https://www.wsj.com/articles/a-deceptive-new-report-on-climate-1509660882

419   Katz, Cheryl. "The Arctic Is Melting Much Faster than Antarctic. That Impacts All of Us." Science, December 4, 2019. https://www.nationalgeographic.com/science/article/arctic

420   Gore, Al. *An inconvenient truth: The crisis of global warming*, p. 109. See Note 20 for more information.

421   USA Today, 12/14/2009,

422   The Guardian, 6/24/2008. Quote by James Hansen. Article by Seth Borenstein, AP.

423   CCR, pp. 225-238.

424   Nsidc.org

425   Search for information on glaciers and retreat of glaciers. https://en.wikipedia.org/wiki/Retreat of glaciers since 1850

426   Gibbens, Sarah. "Melting Glaciers Are Forcing Seas to Rise, New Research Shows." Environment, April 8, 2019. https://www.nationalgeographic.com/environment/article/world-mountain-glaciers-melting-sea-level-rise

427   Our Changing Ocean - inChemistry. "Our Changing Ocean," April 20, 2018. https://inchemistry.acs.org/atomic-news/ocean-acidifcation.html

428   Forbes, Trevor Nace, 2/24/2020.

429   What is coral bleaching? "What Is Coral Bleaching?" https://oceanservice.noaa.gov/facts/coral_bleach.html

430   The claim is "it is getting worse" without any evidence. Kamenos, Nicholas, and Sebastian Hennige. "The Great Barrier Reef Has Been Bleaching for at Least 400 Years, but It's Getting Worse." The Conversation, August 16, 2018. http://theconversation.com/the-great-barrier-reef-has-been-bleaching-for-at-least-400-years-but-its-getting-worse-101691

431   CCR, pp. 216-224.

432   https://reefnation.com/can-coral-reefs-adapt-to-low-ph-conditions/ Nicholas Kamenos and Sebastian Hennige

433   Coral reef image. Woods Hole Oceanographic Institution. https://reefs.com/2017/06/19/lower-ph-found-to-slow-bacterial-coral-disease/

434   How humans are transforming the hurricanes of the future - The Verge. "How Humans Are Transforming the Hurricanes of the Future," November 14, 2018. https://www.theverge.com/2018/11/14/18095236/hurricane-climate-change-harvey-maria-irma-katrina-flooding-rainfall

435   "Climate Goalpost Migration: If You Can't Prove More Hurricanes, Say It's Making Them Relocate." Watts Up With That?, May 5, 2020. https://wattsupwiththat.com/2020/05/05/climate-goalpost-migration-if-you-cant-prove-more-hurricanes-say-its-making-them-relocate/

436   Espinel, Zelde, James P. Kossin, Sandro Galea, Anne S. Richardson, and James M. Shultz. "Forecast: increasing mental health consequences from Atlantic hurricanes throughout the 21st century." *Psychiatric services* 70, no. 12 (2019): 1165-1167. https://ps.psychiatryonline.org/doi/10.1176/appi.ps.201900273

437   Watts Up With That? "What You Need to Know and Are Not Told about Hurricanes," September 15, 2017. https://wattsupwiththat.com/2017/09/15/what-you-need-to-know-and-are-not-told-about-hurricanes/

438   https://reefnation.com/can-coral-reefs-adapt-to-low-ph-conditions/ Nicholas Kamenos and Sebastian Hennige

       See Note 435 for source information. Woods Hole Oceanographic Institution

        See Note 436 for source information.

       "Climate Goalpost Migration: If You Can't Prove More Hurricanes, Say It's Making Them Relocate." Watts Up With That?, May 5, 2020. https://wattsupwiththat.com/2020/05/05/climate-goalpost-migration-if-you-cant-prove-more-hurricanes-say-its-making-them-relocate/

       Espinel, Zelde, James P. Kossin, Sandro Galea, Anne S. Richardson, and James M. Shultz. "Forecast: increasing mental health consequences from Atlantic hurricanes throughout the 21st century." *Psychiatric services* 70, no. 12 (2019): 1165-1167. https://ps.psychiatryonline.org/doi/10.1176/appi.ps.201900273

       Watts Up With That? "What You Need to Know and Are Not Told about Hurricanes," September 15, 2017. https://wattsupwiththat.com/2017/09/15/what-you-need-to-know-and-are-not-told-about-hurricanes/ Watts Up With That? "The Washington Post's Slander on Hurricanes and Climate Change," September 16, 2018. https://wattsupwiththat.com/2018/09/16/the-washington-posts-slander-on-hurricanes-and-climate-change/

439   Tornadoes. NOAA, 2017b.

440   Yang 2014

441   "Statistics | National Interagency Fire Center." https://www.nifc.gov/fire-information/statistics

442   https://lpfw.org/wp-content/uploads/2018/12/2018_Keeley-and-Syphard_Historical-patterns-of-wildfire-
      ignition-sour

443   See Note 193 for more information. https://www.forbes.com/sites/michaelshellenberger/2019/11/04/why-
      everything-they-say-about-california-fires--including-that-climate-matters-most--is-wrong/#278b49fa4cb6

444   Climate Change: Vital Signs of the Planet. "Earth's Freshwater Future: Extremes of Flood and
      Drought – Climate Change: Vital Signs of the Planet." 2022. https://climate.nasa.gov/news/2881/
      earths-freshwater-future-extremes-of-flood-and-drought

445   Competitive Enterprise Institute. "Wrong Again: 50 Years of Failed Eco-Pocalyptic
      Predictions - Competitive Enterprise Institute," September 18, 2019. https://cei.org/blog/
      wrong-again-50-years-of-failed-eco-pocalyptic-predictions/

446   Examples: 1930 US Dust Bowl and 1960s African Sahel

447   The EPA Palmer drought-severity index and the NOAA 2017a charts

448   The Max Planck Institute; de Jong 2013 and Zhu 2016. See Wrightstone, Gregory. *Inconvenient Facts: The
      Science that Al Gore Doesn't Want You to Know*. Silver Crown Productions, LLC, 2017, pp. 66-68.

449   Climate Change 2021: The Physical Science Basis | Climate Change 2021: The Physical Science Basis.
      "Climate Change 2021: The Physical Science Basis." 2021. https://www.ipcc.ch/report/ar6/wg1/

450   Ibid.

451   McCabe and Wolock, "Spatial and Temporal Patterns in Coterminous US streamflow characteristics,"
      Geophysical Research letters, 41 (2014); 6889-97. Quoted from p. 180 in Lukewarming, cited above.

452   Ibid.

453   Search for a list of floods. https://en.wikipedia.org/wiki/List_of_floods

454   By Chinese tradition and mythology, this occurred in 2300 BC.

455   Michaels, Patrick. "Save the Polar Bears? They're Fine, Actually." Cato Institute, 2016. https://www.cato.
      org/publications/commentary/save-polar-bears-theyre-fine-actually
      Video. "The Only Man In The World Who Can Swim With A Polar Bear: Grizzly Man." https://www.
      youtube.com/watch?v=g7rZTZBOrqQ

456   Crockford, S. J. "Twenty good reasons not to worry about polar bears." *Global Warming Policy Foundation
      Briefing Paper* 14 (2015).

457   Lehr, Jay. "Polar Bears: The End of a Climate Delusion Icon - CFACT." CFACT, January 22, 2020. https://
      www.cfact.org/2020/01/22/polar-bears-the-end-of-a-climate-delusion-icon/

458   Polar Bear Science. "Challenging NOAA's 'Arctic Report Card 2014' on Polar Bears," December 19,
      2014. https://polarbearscience.com/2014/12/19/challenging-noaas-arctic-report-card-2014-on-polar-bears/

459   4 Catastrophic Climate Predictions That Never Came True - Foundation for Economic Education. "4
      Catastrophic Climate Predictions That Never Came True | Laura Williams," September 5, 2019. https://fee.
      org/articles/4-catastrophic-climate-predictions-that-never-came-true/

460   Mass Extinction Lie Exposed: Life is Thriving | The Freedom Pub. "Mass Extinction Lie Exposed:
      Life Is Thriving | The Freedom Pub," January 21, 2019. https://blog.heartland.org/2019/05/
      mass-extinction-lie-exposed-life-is-thriving/

461   USA TODAY. "One-Third of All Plant and Animal Species Could Be Extinct in 50
      Years, Study Warns." 2020. https://www.usatoday.com/story/news/nation/2020/02/14/
      climate-change-study-plant-animal-extinction/4760646002/

462   NIPCC, Biological Climate Change

463   Bowhead whale. "Bowhead Whale." https://www.biologicaldiversity.org/species/mammals/bowhead_
      whale/index.html

464   Whale & Dolphin Conservation USA. "Bowhead Whale." https://us.whales.org/whales-dolphins/
      species-guide/bowhead-whale/

465   Gore, Al. *An inconvenient truth: The crisis of global warming*, p. 134. See Note 20 for more information.

466 Leopard seal – Australian Antarctic Program. "Leopard Seal," March 20, 2018. https://www.antarctica.gov.au/about-antarctica/animals/seals/leopard-seal/

467 Search for information on greater white fronted goose. https://www.audubon.org/field-guide/bird/greater-white-fronted-goose

468 Articles on emperor penguins. https://www.nytimes.com/2019/04/25/science/emperor-penguins-antarctica.html

469 Mass Extinction Lie Exposed: Life is Thriving | The Freedom Pub. "Mass Extinction Lie Exposed: Life Is Thriving | The Freedom Pub," January 21, 2019. https://blog.heartland.org/2019/05/mass-extinction-lie-exposed-life-is-thriving/

470 Michael Mann v. Timothy ("Tim") Ball, The Frontier Centre for Public Policy, Inc. and John Doe - Climate Change Litigation (climatecasechart.com)

471 National Review Prevails against Michael Mann. "National Review Prevails against Michael Mann." https://news.yahoo.com/national-review-prevails-against-michael-164216116.html.

472 Watts, Jonathan. "'We Should Be on the Offensive' – James Hansen Calls for Wave of Climate Lawsuits." the Guardian, November 17, 2017. http://www.theguardian.com/environment/2017/nov/17/we-should-be-on-the-offensive-james-hansen-calls-for-wave-of-climate-lawsuits

473 WSJ. 11/9/2015, p. A14.

474 The Nation, 12/13/2019.

475 Deniers is a pejorative name to call anyone because Denier usually refers to those who deny that the Jewish holocaust of WW II existed.

476 Lawrence Solomon, The Deniers, 2010.

477 Robert Carter, Ph.D., former chair of the School of Earth Sciences at James Cook University in Australia (deceased). He wrote over 100 papers, two books, and appeared as expert witness in the U.S. Senate explaining why global warming was not a problem.

   • John Christy, Ph.D., Distinguished Professor of Atmospheric Science and Director of the Earth System Science Center at The University of Alabama in Huntsville

   • Judith Curry, Ph.D., former chair of the School of Earth and Atmospheric Sciences at the Georgia Institute of Technology

   • Freeman Dyson, Ph.D., Professor Emeritus in the Institute for Advanced Study at Princeton University (deceased)

   • Christopher Essex, Ph.D., professor of mathematics at the University of Western Ontario

   • William Gray, Ph.D., professor of atmospheric science at Colorado State University and head of the Tropical Meteorology Project at CSU's Department of Atmospheric Sciences (deceased)

   • William Happer, Ph.D., Cyrus Fogg Brackett Professor of Physics, Emeritus, at Princeton University

   • Christopher Landsea, Ph.D., science and operations officer at the National Hurricane Center

   • David Legates, Ph.D., professor of geography at the University of Delaware and former Director of the Center for Climatic Research

   • Richard Lindzen, Ph.D., Alfred P. Sloan Professor of Meteorology at Massachusetts Institute of Technology (retired)

   • Anthony Lupo, professor of atmospheric sciences at the University of Missouri-Columbia

   • Patrick Michaels, Ph.D., former senior fellow at the Cato Institute, former research professor of environmental sciences at the University of Virginia and past president, the American Association of State Climatologists

   • Cliff Ollier, Ph.D., emeritus professor and honorary research fellow, the School of Earth and Geographical Sciences, University of Western Australia

   • Frederick Seitz, Ph.D., former president of Rockefeller University and the United States National Academy of Sciences (deceased)

   • Nir Shaviv, Ph.D., professor at the Racah Institute of Physics of the Hebrew University of Jerusalem

   • S. Fred Singer, Ph.D., former professor of environmental sciences at the University of Virginia (deceased)

- Willie Soon, Ph.D., physicist/astrophysicist, Solar and Stellar Physics Division of the Harvard–Smithsonian Center for Astrophysics
- Roy Spencer, Ph.D., principal research scientist at The University of Alabama in Huntsville
- Robert Stavins, Ph.D., A.J. Meyer Professor of Energy & Economic Development at the John F. Kennedy School of Government, Harvard University
- Henrik Svensmark, Ph.D., professor in the Division of Solar System Physics at the Danish National Space Institute (DTU Space) in Copenhagen
- Richard S.J. Tol, Ph.D., professor of economics, University of Sussex, and professor of the economics of climate change at the Institute for Environmental Studies and Department of Spatial Economics, Vrije Universiteit, Amsterdam, The Netherlands
- Edward Wegman, Ph.D., professor of statistics, George Mason University (retired)

478   H. Sterling Burnett, Author at ClimateRealism

479   Morano, Marc. "Marc Morano." Climate Depot. https://www.climatedepot.com/author/marcmorano/

480   Search for information on Christopher Horner. https://en.wikipedia.org/wiki/Christopher_C._Horner

481   https://en.wikipedia.org/wiki/Bj percentC3 percentB8rn_Lomborg

482   Christopher Monckton, 3rd Viscount Monckton of Brenchley - Wikipedia. "Christopher Monckton, 3rd Viscount Monckton of Brenchley - Wikipedia," July 20, 2010. https://en.wikipedia.org/wiki/Christopher_Monckton,_3rd_Viscount_Monckton_of_Brenchley

483   Bump, Phillip. "Famed Idiot Lord Monckton Banned for Life from U.N. Climate Talks." Grist, December 7, 2012. https://grist.org/climate-energy/famed-idiot-lord-monckton-banned-for-life-from-un-climate-talks/

484   Independent Australia. "Viscount Christopher Monckton: Lord of the Lies on Climate Change." https://independentaustralia.net/politics/politics-display/viscount-christopher-monckton-lord-of-the-lies-on-climate-change,15179

485   Ibid.

486   Who We Are - Christopher Monckton of Brenchley | Heartland Institute. "Who We Are - Christopher Monckton of Brenchley | Heartland Institute," December 17, 2020. https://www.heartland.org/about-us/who-we-are/lord-christopher-monckton

487   Search for information on Marc Morano. https://en.wikipedia.org/wiki/Marc_Morano

488   Search for information on Matt Ridley. https://en.wikipedia.org/wiki/Matt_Ridley

489   MacDonald, Willard. "It's Easy to Be Tricked by a Climate Denier." Medium, May 2, 2019. https://willardm22.medium.com/its-easy-to-be-tricked-by-a-climate-denier-a87ba4b4a087

490   Wrightstone, Gregory. Inconvenient Facts: The Science that Al Gore Doesn't Want You to Know. Silver Crown Productions, LLC, 2017.

491   Search for information on Gregory Wrightstone. https://www.heartland.org/about-us/who-we-are/gregory-wrightstone

492   Inconvenient Facts #1 Amazon Best Seller on Climate Change." Inconvenient Facts. https://inconvenient-facts.xyz/

493   "Cultural Significance | Polar Bears in Canada." https://www.polarbearscanada.ca/en/polar-bears-canada/cultural-significance.

494   Tyrrell, Martina. "Polar Bears: Climate Change Is a Bigger Threat than Trophy Hunting." The Conversation, May 12, 2016. http://theconversation.com/polar-bears-climate-change-is-a-bigger-threat-than-trophy-hunting-59217

495   Climate at a Glance: Polar Bears. "Climate at a Glance: Polar Bears." https://climateataglance.com/climate-at-a-glance-polar-bears-and-climate

496   Society of Environmental Journalists: SEJournal excerpts. "Society of Environmental Journalists: SEJournal Excerpts." http://www.sejarchive.org/pub/SEJournal_Excerpts_Su08.htm

CHAPTER 6

497   This assumes that Climate Activists use tooth paste and deodorant.

498   o reference necessary. Virtually all Americans know this.

499   Washington Post, 1/13/22 at 11 AM EST

500   Ibid.

501   Ibid.

502   Ibid.

503   Cranky Uncle vs. Climate Change: How to Understand and Respond to Climate ... - John Cook - Google Books

504   Snowfall reports for Virginia. https://www.wfxrtv.com/weather/ noaa-releases-winter-2021-22-outlook-how-much-cold-and-snow-this-year-for-virginia/

505   Jenkins, Jeff. "Parkersburg, Snowshoe Pick up among Highest Snow Totals from Izzy - WV MetroNews." WV MetroNews, January 17, 2022. https://wvmetronews.com/2022/01/17/parkersburg-snowshoe-pick-up-among-highest-snow-totals-from-izzy/
Welch, Sydney. "A Look at Snow Totals across the Area after the Second Winter Storm of the Season." WSET. https://wset.com/weather/weather-extra/weekend-snow-totals-january-17-2022-monday-lynch-burg-roanoke-danville-virginia
First winter storm of 2022 dumped heavy snow across mid-Atlantic on Monday. "First Winter Storm of 2022 Dumped Heavy Snow across Mid-Atlantic on Monday," January 4, 2022. https://www.foxweather.com/weather-news/first-winter-storm-of-2022-dumping-heavy-snow-across-mid-atlantic-on-monday

506   "Snowfall so Far This Season: 2021-2022." https://www.whsv.com/2022/01/08/ snowfall-so-far-this-season-2021-2022/

507   What are the major sources and users of energy in the United States? | American Geosciences Institute

508   US EPA. "Global Greenhouse Gas Emissions Data | US EPA," January 12, 2016. https://www.epa.gov/ ghgemissions/global-greenhouse-gas-emissions-data

509   Separating Myth from Reality: A Closer Look at the Energy Efficiency Panacea (ensec.org)

510   Pew Research Center. "Renewable Energy Is Growing Fast in the U.S., but Fossil Fuels Still Dominate," January 15, 2020. https://www.pewresearch.org/fact-tank/2020/01/15/ renewable-energy-is-growing-fast-in-the-u-s-but-fossil-fuels-still-dominate/

511   Use of electricity - U.S. Energy Information Administration (EIA). "Use of Electricity - U.S. Energy Information Administration (EIA)," November 17, 2022. https://www.eia.gov/energyexplained/electricity/ use-of-electricity.php

512   Henderson, Michael I., Damir Novosel, and Mariesa L. Crow. "Electric power grid modernization trends, challenges, and opportunities." In IEEE, Nov. 2017. https://www.cmu.edu/epp/irle/readings/henderson-novosel-crow-electric-power-grid-modernization.pdf

513   Cohn, Charlotte. "The Cost of Saving Electricity for the Largest U.S. Utilities: Ratepay." The Cost of Saving Electricity for the Largest U.S. Utilities: Ratepayer-Funded Efficiency Programs in 2018 | ACEEE, 2021. https://www.aceee.org/topic-brief/2021/06/ cost-saving-electricity-largest-us-utilities-ratepayer-funded-efficiency.

514   "Electricity Rates By State - EnergyBot." https://www.energybot.com/electricity-rates-by-state.html

515   Lewis, Marlo. "How Much Will the Green New Deal Cost Your Family? - Competitive Enterprise Institute." Competitive Enterprise Institute, February 26, 2019. https://cei.org/blog/ how-much-will-the-green-new-deal-cost-your-family/

516   "Frequently Asked Questions (FAQs) - U.S. Energy Information Administration (EIA)," November 17, 2022. https://www.eia.gov/tools/faqs/faq.php. (US Energy Information Administration).

517   "Study: Corn Ethanol May Be Worse For Climate Than Gasoline," February 16, 2022. https://freerepublic. com/focus/f-bloggers/4038672/posts

518   International Energy Agency. https://www.iea.org/reports/fuel-consumption-of-cars-and-vans

519   Seto, J.L. "The Average Fuel Economy of Cars Has Risen a Shocking Amount in the Last 10 Years." MotorBiscuit, February 15, 2020. https://www.motorbiscuit.com/ the-average-fuel-economy-of-cars-has-risen-a-shocking-amount-in-the-last-10-years/

520   International Energy Agency. https://www.iea.org/reports/fuel-consumption-of-cars-and-vans

521   Power technology.com

522   Electric cars may use less fuel while in operation but they consume more CO than gasoline cars in their manufacture and disposal. https://www.europarl.europa.eu/news/en/headlines/society/20190313STO31218/CO$_2$-emissions-from-cars-facts-and-figures-infographics

523   Environment & Climate News, Oct 2021, p. 20.

524   Ibid.

525   Two trillion gallons: Fuel savings from fuel economy improvements to US light-duty vehicles, 1975–2018 - ScienceDirect. "Two Trillion Gallons: Fuel Savings from Fuel Economy Improvements to US Light-Duty Vehicles, 1975–2018," April 25, 2020. https://www.sciencedirect.com/science/article/abs/pii/S0301421520302627
https://doi.org/10.1016/j.enpol.2020.111517t-the-gro

526   https://www.truckinginfo.com/311831/fleets-hit-7-28-mpg.-average-in-latest-nacfe-report

527   Electric Vehicle Guide. "New Truck Standards: Opportunity to Cut Fuel Consumption 40% by 2025," January 1, 2022. https://content.sierraclub.org/evguide/blog/2014/05/new-truck-standards-opportunity-cut-fuel-consumption-40-2025

528   Search on fuel efficiency. https://en.wikipedia.org/wiki/Fuel_efficiency

529   "The Growth in Greenhouse Gas Emissions from Commercial Aviation" (2019, Revised 2022) | White Papers | EESI, June 9, 2022. https://www.eesi.org/papers/view/fact-sheeth-in-greenhouse-gas-emissions-from-commercial-aviation

530   Financial Times. "Aircraft Emissions Fall Sharply as Pandemic Grounds Flights." https://www.ft.com/content/c736cd3c-1457-440b-af07-4061afb35bc9

531   UN News. "Air Travel down 60 per Cent, as Airline Industry Losses Top $370 Billion: ICAO," January 15, 2021. https://news.un.org/en/story/2021/01/1082302

532   "Use of Energy in Explained - U.S. Energy Information Administration (EIA)," November 17, 2022. https://www.eia.gov/energyexplained/use-of-energy/

533   Center for Climate and Energy Solutions. "Controlling Industrial Greenhouse Gas Emissions." https://www.c2es.org/content/regulating-industrial-sector-carbon-emissions/

534   "Use of Energy in Industry - U.S. Energy Information Administration (EIA)," November 17, 2022. https://www.eia.gov/energyexplained/use-of-energy/industry.php.

535   (Climate Change News) You look it up. I am busy now.

536   https://www.vxchnge.com/blog/growing-energy-demands-of-data-centers

537   Courtesy of LiquidCool Solutions, Rochester, MN. Note that the author has a financial interest in this company.

538   Life:Powered. "Benefits of Fossil Fuels for Agricultural Production - Life:Powered," October 12, 2018. https://lifepowered.org/benefits-of-fossil-fuels-for-agricultural-production/

539   Bader, Zach. "How Agriculture Will Reduce Its Greenhouse Gas Emissions by 50% over the next Five Years." iowafarmbureau.com, February 11, 2020. https://www.iowafarmbureau.com/Article/How-agriculture-will-reduce-its-greenhouse-gas-emissions-by-50-over-the-next-five-years

540   "Energy Efficiency for Agriculture." https://www.shipleyenergy.com/energy-101-guides/guide/2018/09/19/energy-efficiency-for-agriculture

541   Prentice, Neil. "The 5 Top Ways Drones Can Cut Greenhouse Gas (GHG) Emissions." Medium, August 22, 2018. https://medium.com/soar-earth/the-5-top-ways-drones-can-cut-greenhouse-gas-ghg-emissions-853def950995

542   "Use of Energy in Industry - U.S. Energy Information Administration (EIA)," November 17, 2022. https://www.eia.gov/energyexplained/use-of-energy/industry.php

543   "Use of Energy in Industry - U.S. Energy Information Administration (EIA)," November 17, 2022. https://www.eia.gov/energyexplained/use-of-energy/industry.php

544   Courtesy of Intellihot water heaters, Peoria Illinois. Note that the author has a financial interest in this company.

545   Project Veritas End of Year 2021, p. 13.

546   "Renewable Energy vs Fossil Fuels: Learn About Costs, Subsidies & More | Inspire Clean Energy." https://www.inspirecleanenergy.com/blog/clean-energy-101/renewable-energy-vs-fossil-fuels

547 CCR, pp. 299-308, 341-360, and 733-741. CCR stands for Climate Change Reconsidered published by the National Nongovernmental International Panel on Climate Change (NIPCC) 2019, which is a text book, probably the greatest single book source of accurate climate knowledge that I have ever seen

548 World energy consumption by energy source 2050 | Statista

549 Ibid.

550 Pew Research Center. "Renewable Energy Is Growing Fast in the U.S., but Fossil Fuels Still Dominate," January 15, 2020. https://www.pewresearch.org/fact-tank/2020/01/15/renewable-energy-is-growing-fast-in-the-u-s-but-fossil-fuels-still-dominate/

551 Ibid.

552 "Energy Source." http://piperrconnors.weebly.com/energy-source.html

553 "Electricity in the U.S. - U.S. Energy Information Administration (EIA)," November 17, 2022. https://www.eia.gov/energyexplained/electricity/electricity-in-the-us.php

554 Timmons, David, Jonathan M. Harris, and Brian Roach. "The economics of renewable energy." *Global Development And Environment Institute, Tufts University* 52 (2014): 1-52. https://www.bu.edu/eci/files/2019/06/RenewableEnergyEcon.pdf

555 Ibid.

556 Ibid.

557 Energy.gov. "Hydropower Vision Report: Full Report," October 21, 2016. https://www.energy.gov/eere/water/downloads/hydropower-vision-report-full-report

558 "Electricity in the U.S. - U.S. Energy Information Administration (EIA)," November 17, 2022. https://www.eia.gov/energyexplained/electricity/electricity-in-the-us.php

559 Op. Cit. CCR. Revisited 2. p. 351]

560 "Nuclear Power in France | French Nuclear Energy - World Nuclear Association." https://www.world-nuclear.org/information-library/country-profiles/countries-a-f/france.aspx

561 Shellenberger, Michael. "If Saving The Climate Requires Making Energy So Expensive, Why Is French Electricity So Cheap?" Forbes, February 5, 2019. https://www.forbes.com/sites/michaelshellenberger/2019/02/05/if-saving-the-climate-requires-making-energy-so-expensive-why-is-french-electricity-so-cheap/

562 https://energycentral.com/c/ec/germany-solar-and-wind-triple-cost-france percentE2 per-cent80 percent99s-nuclear-and-will-last-half-long

563 German electricity was nearly 10 times dirtier than France's in 2016 — Environmental Progress

564 "World's First Small Modular Nuclear Reactor Starts Producing Energy in China." January 4, 2022. https://interestingengineering.com/science/the-worlds-first-small-modular-nuclear-reactor-is-sending-power-to-the-grid

565 American Bird conservatory. Epoch times, 5/18/22. p. A32.

566 https://windmillskill.com/blog/windfarms-kill-10-20-times-more-previously-thought. It should be pointed out that advocates of windmills claim a much smaller number like one-million.

567 https://windmillskill.com/blog/windfarms-kill-10-20-times-more-previously-thought. It should be pointed out that advocates of windmills claim a much smaller number like one-million.

568 "How Many Turbines Are Contained in the U.S. Wind Turbine Database? | U.S. Geological Survey," July 23, 2019. https://www.usgs.gov/faqs/how-many-turbines-are-contained-us-wind-turbine-database?qt-news_science_products=0#qt-news_science_products

569 Ibid.

570 Sciencing. "How Much Land Is Needed for Wind Turbines?," May 10, 2018. https://sciencing.com/much-land-needed-wind-turbines-12304634.html

571 Ibid.

572 Barnard, Michael. "How Many Wind Turbines Would It Take To Power The US?" Forbes, December 18, 2019. https://www.forbes.com/sites/quora/2019/12/18/how-many-wind-turbines-would-it-take-to-power-the-us/

573 See Prager U Mark Mills

574   Ibid.

575   In Germany it is believed that 20 percent of the 30,000 turbines were abandoned in 2020 due to maintenance needs general wear and tear as the electrical output was severely reduced. The Heartland Institute Policy Brief, December 2019, p. 20.

576   Removing a 3 MW turbine is a monumental task because the machine and the concrete base weigh 3,000 tons The Heartland Institute Policy Brief, December 2019, p. 19.

577   Sreevani, P. "Wood as a renewable source of energy and future fuel." In *AIP Conference Proceedings*, vol. 1992, no. 1, p. 040007. AIP Publishing LLC, 2018. https://aip.scitation.org/doi/10.1063/1.5047972

578   Garthwaite, Josie. "Soils or Plants Will Absorb More CO2 as Carbon Levels Rise – but Not Both, Stanford Study Finds." Soils or plants will absorb more CO2 as carbon levels rise – but not both, Stanford study finds. https://news.stanford.edu/press/view/38728

579   "Political Calculations: Inventions in Everything: Mechanical Trees," February 13, 2020. https://politicalcal-culations.blogspot.com/2020/02/inventions-in-everything-mechanical.html#.X-DuomDtyUk

580   "Election Fraud? Patty Schachtner Was Not Confined - Empower Wisconsin." Empower Wisconsin, December 20, 2020. https://empowerwisconsin.org/election-fraud-patty-schachtner-was-not-confined/

581   "Is the 'Trillion Trees Act' Remotely Possible?" https://www.triplepundit.com/story/2020/trillion-trees-act-remotely-possible/86636

582   "Science | AAAS." https://www.sciencemag.org/news/2017/01/wood-green-source-energy-scientists-are-divided

583   Anthony Watts/ Nature WorldNews 3/2/15. According to Ruby Evenson, deputy Chief of Communications for the Nevada Bureau of Land Management (NBLM) in Reon , as reported by Re Wire.

584   Kennedy, David. "Nevada's 110 Megawatt Crescent Dunes Solar Project Now Fully Online - Canadian Manufacturing." Canadian Manufacturing, February 23, 2016. https://www.canadianmanufacturing.com/technology/nevadas-110-mw-crescent-dunes-solar-project-goes-fully-online-162871/

585   The Heartland Institute Policy Brief, December 2019, p. 19.

586   "Electricity in the U.S. - U.S. Energy Information Administration (EIA)," November 17, 2022. https://www.eia.gov/energyexplained/electricity/electricity-in-the-us.php

587   WSJ, 5/28/22, p. A12.

588   WSJ, 5/28/22, p. A11.

589   Michael Moore's movie Planet of the Humans discussed Wind farms and their use of energy. Watch the 4 minute video. https://www.youtube.com/watch?v=Zk11vI-7czE

590   See Prager U Mark Mills

591   The Epoch Times, 5/25/22, p. A15.

592   Lea, Robert. "How Hot Is the Sun?" Space.com, January 21, 2022. https://www.space.com/17137-how-hot-is-the-sun.html

593   Ibid.

594   John Cook in Grumpy Uncle Op. Cit.

595   Climate Change: Incoming Sunlight | NOAA Climate.gov

596   "Electricity Consumption - an Overview | ScienceDirect Topics." https://www.sciencedirect.com/topics/engineering/electricity-consumption

597   C-CHANGE | Harvard T.H. Chan School of Public Health. "Fossil Fuels & Health," January 7, 2019. https://www.hsph.harvard.edu/c-change/subtopics/fossil-fuels-health/

598   "Fossil Fuels Kill Nearly 9 Million Annually, More Than Twice Previous Estimate, Study Finds - EcoWatch," February 9, 2021. https://www.ecowatch.com/fossil-fuels-air-pollution-deaths-2650416201.html

599   Worldwide the claims seem to range from about 5 million to 9 million deaths by fossil fuels, but the reasoning is the same, so I am only addressing the U.S. in this edition of my book. See: https://www.ecowatch.com/fossil-fuels-air-pollution-deaths-2650416201.html https://ourworldindata.org/data-review-air-pollution-deaths

600   FastStats - Homicide. "FastStats," September 6, 2022. https://www.cdc.gov/nchs/fastats/homicide.htm

601   From the EPA

Percent Change in Air Quality

	1980 vs 2020	1990 vs 2020	2000 vs 2020	2010 vs 2020
Carbon Monoxide	-81	-73	-57	-12
Lead	-98	-98	-93	-86
Nitrogen Dioxide (annual)	-67	-61	-53	-29
Nitrogen Dioxide (1-hour)	-64	-54	-39	-21
Ozone (8-hour)	-33	-25	-20	-10
PM_{10} (24-hour)	---	-26	-27	+9
$PM_{2.5}$ (annual)	---	---	-41	-18
$PM_{2.5}$ (24-hour)	---	---	-30	+3
Sulfur Dioxide (1-hour)	-94	-91	-85	-74

602   EPA. "Our Nation's Air 2016." Our Nation's Air 2016. https://gispub.epa.gov/air/trendsreport/2016/

603   EPA. "History of Air Pollution | US EPA." US EPA, September 4, 2014. https://www.epa.gov/air-research/history-air-pollution

604   Yale Climate Connections. "Yale Climate Connections," 2022. http://yaleclimateconnections.org/

605   EPA. "Air Quality - National Summary | US EPA." US EPA, May 4, 2016. https://www.epa.gov/air-trends/air-quality-national-summary

606   Search for deaths related to heart disease. https://www.google.com/search?q=How+many+people+died+of+heart+disease+in+united+states&ie=UTF-8&oe=UTF-8&hl=en-us&client=safari

607   "Los Angeles County Heart Disease Statistics | LiveStories." https://www.livestories.com/statistics/california/los-angeles-county-heart-disease-deaths-mortality

608   Ibid.

609   "Orleans Parish Heart Disease Statistics | LiveStories." https://www.livestories.com/statistics/louisiana/orleans-parish-heart-disease-deaths-mortality

610   Search for deaths related to heart disease in Philadelphia. https://www.google.com/search?q=How+many+people+die+of+heart+disease+in+philadelphia&ie=UTF-8&oe=UTF-8&hl=en-us&client=safari

611   Planet of the Humans - Rotten Tomatoes
        Michael Moore's Planet of the Humans gets clean energy and climate activism terribly wrong - Vox

612   Michael Moore's 'Planet of the Humans' documentary peddles dangerous climate denial » Yale Climate Connections

613   Planet of the Humans review - Google Search.

614   Currently on Amazon Prime. Apparently censored from Netflix because it supports the "wrong" side.

CHAPTER 7

615   Le Quéré, Corinne, Robert B. Jackson, Matthew W. Jones, Adam JP Smith, Sam Abernethy, Robbie M. Andrew, Anthony J. De-Gol et al. "Temporary reduction in daily global CO 2 emissions during the COVID-19 forced confinement." *Nature climate change* 10, no. 7 (2020): 647-653. https://www.nature.com/articles/s41558-020-0797-x

616   "Global Monitoring Laboratory - Carbon Cycle Greenhouse Gases." https://www.esrl.noaa.gov/gmd/ccgg/covid2.html

617   U.S. Energy Information Administration - EIA - Independent Statistics and Analysis. "U.S. Fossil Fuel Consumption Fell by 9% in 2020, the Lowest Level in Nearly 30 Years," November 17, 2022. https://www.eia.gov/todayinenergy/detail.php?id=48596

618   WSJ. 3/18/21, p. B11

619   Search for world temperatures in April of 2020. https://.google.com/search?q=world+temperatures+april+2020&ie=UTF-8&oe=UTF-8&hl=en-us&client=safari

620   Stein, Theo. "Rise of Carbon Dioxide Unabated." Welcome to NOAA Research, June 4, 2020. https://research.noaa.gov/article/ArtMID/587/ArticleID/2636/Rise-of-carbon-dioxide-unabated

621   Lomborg, Bjorn. "How the Climate Elite Spread Misery." *Wall Street Journal*, Jul 22, 2022.

622   Biology Stack Exchange. "How Precisely Can We Sense Temperature Differences?," March 31, 2015. https://biology.stackexchange.com/questions/30952/how-precisely-can-we-sense-temperature-differences

623   HadCRUT4 data, May 2016 to January 2021

624   Search for information on Atlantic hurricane season. https://en.wikipedia.org/wiki/2020_Atlantic_hurricane_season

625   U.S. Energy Information Administration - EIA - Independent Statistics and Analysis. "U.S. Fossil Fuel Consumption Fell by 9% in 2020, the Lowest Level in Nearly 30 Years," November 17, 2022. https://www.eia.gov/todayinenergy/detail.php?id=48596

626   Fossil fuel use US 2020 vs 2021 - Search (bing.com)

627   Active 2021 Atlantic hurricane season officially ends | National Oceanic and Atmospheric Administration (noaa.gov). https://www.noaa.gov/news-release/active-2021-atlantic-hurricane-season-officially-ends

628   Search for information on August Complex wildfire. https://en.wikipedia.org/wiki/August_Complex_fire

629   Search for information on wildfire season. https://en.wikipedia.org/wiki/2020_Western_United_States_wildfire_season

630   People Cause Most U.S. Wildfires. "People Cause Most U.S. Wildfires," March 6, 2017. https://earthobservatory.nasa.gov/images/89757/people-cause-most-us-wildfires

631   US forest fires 2020 compared to 2021 - Search (bing.com). https://www.bing.com/search?q=Us+forest+fires+2020+compared+to+2021&cvid=6717e57666474576881aa01531991f32&aqs=edge..69i57.23976j0j9&FORM=ANAB01&PC=U531

632   Kurtzleben, Danielle. "Rep. Alexandria Ocasio-Cortez Releases Green New Deal Outline." NPR.org, February 7, 2019. https://www.npr.org/2019/02/07/691997301/rep-alexandria-ocasio-cortez-releases-green-new-deal-outline

633   Holtz-Eakin, Douglas, Dan Bosch, Ben Gitis, Dan Goldbeck, and Phillip Rossetti. "The Green New Deal: Scope, Scale, and Implications - AAF." AAF, February 25, 2019. https://www.americanactionforum.org/research/the-green-new-deal-scope-scale-and-implications/

634   Wikipedia

635   "Poll: Most Americans want universal healthcare but don't want to abolish private insurance." TheHill. https://thehill.com/hilltv/what-americas-thinking/428958-poll-voters-want-the-government-to-provide-healthcare-for

636   "More Americans now favor single payer health coverage than in 2019." Pew Research Center. https://www.pewresearch.org/fact-tank/2020/09/29/increasing-share-of-americans-favor-a-single-government-program-to-provide-health-care-coverage/

637   "Public Opinion on Single-Payer, National Health Plans, and Expanding Access to Medicare Coverage." KFF. https://www.kff.org/slideshow/public-opinion-on-single-payer-national-health-plans-and-expanding-access-to-medicare-coverage/

638   "The catastrophic costs of socialist policies." Fox Business. https://www.foxbusiness.com/business-leaders/socialist-policies-ocasio-cortez-green-new-deal

639   It is clear to me that the Progressive Left has spent 30 years convincing most of us to be fearful and worried about climate change and global warming. Most of the mass media, the social media, the universities and many of our most important government agencies believe, and the preponderance of their messages support justifications for activist measures to prevent the claimed climate change. They have succeeded in convincing most of us that climate change is a major problem.

However, The Progressive Left has not succeeded in convincing the majority of Americans that the government should provide "free" health care, guaranteed jobs for all, and free food for more Americans. There is a very strong contingent in the U.S. who believe in traditional American values including that real achievement, self-fulfillment, and happiness can only result from hard work and persistent dedicated efforts; that self-responsibility and personal freedom together with individuals making decisions for themselves is better than government decision making; that merit and self-responsibility combined with personal freedom provide us with a better life and a better future.

Most Americans have little interest in supporting guaranteed jobs, universal healthcare, or food security. They prefer individual Americans to use their personal monies to support personal charities which provide health, jobs, and food support. They believe this is less expensive, more efficient, and more personally rewarding than government handouts and support.

Thus, The Progressive Left hides, disguises, and camouflages their real goals by pretending they are saving us from cataclysmic global warming and climate change.

Historically there has never been a country which spends significantly more than its income, takes on huge debt that it has little chance to repay without generating enormous inflation. America during the past 50 years has had the benefit of being the reserve currency of the world. Entire nations use our currency as their own and thereby enable the United States to be less responsible in its financial decisions. We already have $30 trillion of debt. How long we can continue along this path without a national bankruptcy? History has never produced a country or empire that has succeeded with this lack of fiscal responsibility.

I don't want to predict whether or not the United States will be able to survive this huge financial federal debt crisis. However, spending perhaps $100 trillion to promote programs we cannot afford makes little sense.

Regarding payments, let me address both the sources and amounts of energy funding. And let me start with a discussion of Capitalism and Socialism, without taking sides as to whether either is more desirable. There are numerous definitions of Socialism, many of which are complicated and contradictory. For this writing, let me define Socialism as the economic system which believes that government through its experts and taxes and debt knows best how to provide people with goods and services. It is the government which decides how much money should be transferred from the rich to the poor (or from the less rich to the more rich). Socialist philosophy is that expert government people are necessary because the common person needs a "guiding hand" so that they will do what is in their best interest.

Capitalism, on the other hand, is the economic system which provides goods and services though willing buyers and sellers and, as Adam Smith wrote, uses an "invisible hand" that guides us to be reasonable in order to enhance the possibilities of a voluntary transaction. In other words, in Capitalism each individual is responsible for providing their own money to pay for the energy they use. Under Socialism the government using taxes and debt provides energy for everyone regardless of individual payments based upon individual perceived needs and payments are compulsory.

Virtually all governments have both components, both Socialist and Capitalist and it is the balance between them that is important. For example, the U.S. Medicare system is a hybrid example where Government primarily pays the bills and Private Industry provides the service. As a result, because for the most part, the U.S. government is inefficient (it isn't their money and the costs are high) and the quality of private, in general, exceptionally high compared to the rest of the world.

640   https://www.gao.gov/key_issues/reducing_greenhouse gas_emissions/issue_summary

641   Lewis, Marlo. "How Much Will the Green New Deal Cost Your Family? - Competitive Enterprise Institute." Competitive Enterprise Institute, February 26, 2019. https://cei.org/blog/how-much-will-the-green-new-deal-cost-your-family/

642   Delingpole, James. "Worst Deal In History: $1.5 Trillion A Year To Reduce Global Warming By 0.048°C." Breitbart, November 10, 2015. https://www.breitbart.com/politics/2015/11/10/cost-climate-change-1-5-trillion-year-reduce-global-warming-0-048c/

643   Ibid.

644   The Paris Agreement had a stated goal of reducing CO_2 emissions by 20 percent. In June 2017, President Donald Trump announced the United States would withdraw from the Paris Agreement, arguing at the time that it would impose a disproportionate burden on the United States and do little to stop global warming. One of President Joe Biden's first acts upon taking office was to declare the United States was once again a member of the agreement, even though the U.S. Senate has yet to vote on whether or not to approve the "treaty." The debate over the Paris Agreement and the frequent "Conferences of the Parties" (COPs) have been occasions for raising many of the false claims and predictions addressed earlier in this book (Joe Bast, November 2021 comment)

645   Search for information on the Paris Agreement. https://en.wikipedia.org/wiki/Paris_Agreement

646   Plumer, Brad, and Nadja Popovich. "Why Half a Degree of Global Warming Is a Big Deal (Published 2018)." Why Half a Degree of Global Warming Is a Big Deal - The New York Times, October 8, 2018. https://www.nytimes.com/interactive/2018/10/07/climate/ipcc-report-half-degree.html

647   "Paris Temperature Goal."https://climateactiontracker.org/methodology/paris-temperature-goal/?back=https%3A%2F%2Fwww.google.com%2Fsearch%3Fclient%3Dsafari%26as_qdr%3Dall%26as_occt%3Dany%26safe%3Dactive%26as_q%3DWhat+is+the+date+that+we+must+hit+one+.5%C2%B0C+according+to+the+Paris+agreement%26channel%3Daplab%26source%3Da-app1%26hl%3Den

648   The 2 °C Global Temperature Target and the Evolution of the Long-Term Goal of Addressing Climate Change—From the United Nations Framework Convention on Climate Change to the Paris Agreement - ScienceDirect. "The 2 °C Global Temperature Target and the Evolution of the Long-Term Goal of Addressing Climate Change—From the United Nations Framework Convention on Climate Change to the Paris Agreement," May 12, 2017. https://www.sciencedirect.com/science/article/pii/S2095809917303077

649   Ibid.

650   https://www.spg.lobal.com/en/research-insights/articles/what-s-the-deal-with-the-2-degree-scenario

651   Plumer, Brad, and Nadja Popovich. "Why Half a Degree of Global Warming Is a Big Deal (Published 2018)." Why Half a Degree of Global Warming Is a Big Deal - The New York Times, October 8, 2018. https://www.nytimes.com/interactive/2018/10/07/climate/ipcc-report-half-degree.html "Paris Temperature Goal." https://climateactiontracker.org/methodology/paris-temperature-goal/?back=https%3A%2F%2Fwww.google.com%2Fsearch%3Fclient%3Dsafari%26as_qdr%3Dall%26as_occt%3Dany%26safe%3Dactive%26as_q%3DWhat+is+the+date+that+we+must+hit+one+.5%C2%B0C+according+to+the+Paris+agreement%26channel%3Daplab%26source%3Da-app1%26hl%3Den

652   Note that earlier in the chapter, we explained and cited references that there was an 8% reduction of this amount of fossil fuel during the 2020 Covid pandemic which resulted in no reduction in the rate of temperature increase or hurricanes or wildfires.

653   https://www.spg.lobal.com/en/research-insights/articles/what-s-the-deal-with-the-2-degree-scenario

654   Plumer, Brad, and Nadja Popovich. "Why Half a Degree of Global Warming Is a Big Deal (Published 2018)." Why Half a Degree of Global Warming Is a Big Deal - The New York Times, October 8, 2018. https://www.nytimes.com/interactive/2018/10/07/climate/ipcc-report-half-degree.html

655   The Paris climate pact is 5 years old. Is it working? | Science | AAAS. "The Paris Climate Pact Is 5 Years Old. Is It Working?," December 11, 2020. https://www.science.org/content/article/paris-climate-pact-5-years-old-it-working

656   Search for information on the Paris Agreement. https://www.google.com/search?q=paris+agreement+2050&ie=UTF-8&oe=UTF-8&hl=en-us&client=safari

657   Renewable puzzle. http://www.renewablepuzzle.com/

658   Harvey, Fiona. "China's Five-Year Plan Could Push Emissions Higher Unless Action Is Taken." the Guardian, March 5, 2021. http://www.theguardian.com/world/2021/mar/05/china-five-year-plan-emissions

659   Time. "China Is Planning 43 New Coal-Fired Power Plants. Can It Still Keep Its Promises to Cut Emissions?," August 20, 2021. https://time.com/6090732/china-coal-power-plants-emissions/

660   IEO2021 Chart Library: Coal (eia.gov). "Real GDP growth rate by year in the U.S." Statista. https://www.eia.gov/outlooks/ieo/pdf/IEO2021_ChartLibrary_Coal.pdf

661   Renewable puzzle. http://www.renewablepuzzle.com/

662   Harvey, Fiona. "China's Five-Year Plan Could Push Emissions Higher Unless Action Is Taken." the Guardian, March 5, 2021. http://www.theguardian.com/world/2021/mar/05/china-five-year-plan-emission

663   Time. "China Is Planning 43 New Coal-Fired Power Plants. Can It Still Keep Its Promises to Cut Emissions?," August 20, 2021. https://time.com/6090732/china-coal-power-plants-cmissions/

664   IEO2021 Chart Library: Coal (eia.gov); "Real GDP growth rate by year in the U.S." Statista. https://www.eia.gov/outlooks/ieo/pdf/IEO2021_ChartLibrary_Coal.pdf

665   Search for information on Paris Agreement. https://en.wikipedia.org/wiki/Paris_Agreement

666   "Global CO2 emissions fall in 2009, but the past decade still sees rapid emissions growth." Grist. https://grist.org/article/global-carbon-dioxide-emissions-fall-in-2009-past-decade-still-sees-rapid-e/#:~:text=In%20 2009%2C%20carbon%20dioxide%20%28CO2%29%20emissions%20in%20China,in%202008%20to%20 8.4%20billion%20tons%20in%202009

       Roser, Max, and Esteban Ortiz-Ospina. "Literacy." Our World in Data. https://ourworldindata.org/literacy

667   Real GDP growth rate by year in the U.S. | Statistica.

668   "COVID-19 pandemic cut life expectancy by most since World War Two – study." Reuters. https://www.reuters.com/business/healthcare-pharmaceuticals/covid-19-pandemic-cut-life-expectancy-by-most-since-world-war-two-study-2021-09-26/

669   Greenhalgh, Jane. "U.S. Life Expectancy Fell By 1.5 Years In 2020, The Biggest Drop Since WWII." NPR.org, July 21, 2021. https://www.npr.org/sections/coronavirus-live-updates/2021/07/21/1018590263/u-s-life-expectancy-fell-1-5-years-2020-biggest-drop-since-ww-ii-covid

670   "Poverty data." World Bank. https://data.worldbank.org/topic/11
       "Poverty." World Bank. https://data.worldbank.org/topic/poverty

671   Roser, Max, and Esteban Ortiz-Ospina. "Literacy." Our World in Data. https://ourworldindata.org/literacy

672   "United States: life expectancy 1860-2020." Statista. https://www.statista.com/statistics/1040079/life-expectancy-united-states-all-time/

673   "United States: life expectancy 1860-2020." Statista. https://www.statista.com/statistics/1040079/life-expectancy-united-states-all-time

674   Taken from Our World in Data, Max Roser. (Source: USDA, Economic Research Service, Food Expenditure Series)
       Diamandis, MD, Peter H. "Why the World Is Better Than You Think in 10 Powerful Charts." Singularity Hub, June 27, 2016. https://singularityhub.com/2016/06/27/why-the-world-is-better-than-you-think-in-10-powerful-charts/

675   Ibid.

676   Taken from Our World in Data, Max Roser. (Source: USDA, Economic Research Service, Food Expenditure Series)
       Diamandis, MD, Peter H. "Why the World Is Better Than You Think in 10 Powerful Charts." Singularity Hub, June 27, 2016. https://singularityhub.com/2016/06/27/why-the-world-is-better-than-you-think-in-10-powerful-charts/

677   Mauna Loa report. See Berkeley Earth.

678   "Rise of Carbon Dioxide in the Atmosphere Continues Unabated | Earth | EarthSky," June 9, 2020. https://earthsky.org/earth/rising-carbon-dioxide-co2-record-high-june2020/

679   https://www.farsnews.ir/en/news/13990204000132/Rising-Carbn-Dixide-May-Impair-Cgniin

680   Search for information on carbon dioxide. https://en.wikipedia.org/wiki/Carbon_dioxide

681   "Exposure Limits for Carbon Dioxide Gas – CO2 Limits." InspectAPedia.com. http://www.inspectapedia.com/hazmat/CO2_Exposure_Limits.htm

682   "Wildfires Not Caused by 'Climate Change,' States Doctors for Disaster Preparedness." https://www.prnewswire.com/news-releases/wildfires-not-caused-by-climate-change-states-doctors-for-disaster-pre-paredness-301131756.html

683   The Guardian. "The Heat Is on over the Climate Crisis. Only Radical Measures Will Work," May 18, 2019. http://www.theguardian.com/environment/2019/may/18/climate-crisis-heat-is-on-global-heating-four-degrees-2100-change-way-we-live

684   In my opinion, any educator that suggests that we might have 125 foot higher oceans from a small increase in temperature should not be teaching until she receives significant re-education.

685   Plumer, Brad, and Nadja Popovich. "Why Half a Degree of Global Warming Is a Big Deal (Published 2018)." Why Half a Degree of Global Warming Is a Big Deal - The New York Times, October 8, 2018. https://www.nytimes.com/interactive/2018/10/07/climate/ipcc-report-half-degree.html

686   (Examples: 1930 US Dust Bowl and 1960s African Sahel).

687   The Max Planck Institute; de Jong 2013 and Zhu 2016. See Wrightstone, Gregory. *Inconvenient Facts: The Science that Al Gore Doesn't Want You to Know*. Silver Crown Productions, LLC, 2017, pp. 66-68.

688   Ibid.

689   Ibid. Johan Rockström, director of the Potsdam Institute for Climate Impact Research in Germany.

690   Ibid.

691   Search for information on ocean fishes. https://oceana.org/marine-life/ocean-fishes

692   Search for information on the Atlantic cod. https://oceana.org/marine-life/ocean-fishes/atlantic-cod

693   https://reefnation.com/can-coral-reefs-adapt-to-low-ph-conditions/. Also, the calcium carbonate saturation state is lower which also is supposed to weaken the coral reef skeleton

694   The Guardian. "The Heat Is on over the Climate Crisis. Only Radical Measures Will Work," May 18, 2019. http://www.theguardian.com/environment/2019/may/18/climate-crisis-heat-is-on-global-heating-four-degrees-2100-change-way-we-live
Daniel Rothman, co-director of MIT's Lorenz Center

695   Plumer, Brad, and Nadja Popovich. "Why Half a Degree of Global Warming Is a Big Deal (Published 2018)." Why Half a Degree of Global Warming Is a Big Deal - The New York Times, October 8, 2018. https://www.nytimes.com/interactive/2018/10/07/climate/ipcc-report-half-degree.html

696   I have always said, "There is nothing worse than crowded insects."

697   Search for teaching resources. Smithsonian National Museum of Natural History. "Extinction Over Time." http://naturalhistory.si.edu/education/teaching-resources/paleontology/extinction-over-time

698   The Guardian. "The Heat Is on over the Climate Crisis. Only Radical Measures Will Work," May 18, 2019. http://www.theguardian.com/environment/2019/may/18/climate-crisis-heat-is-on-global-heating-four-degrees-2100-change-way-we-live

699   Plumer, Brad, and Nadja Popovich. "Why Half a Degree of Global Warming Is a Big Deal (Published 2018)." Why Half a Degree of Global Warming Is a Big Deal - The New York Times, October 8, 2018. https://www.nytimes.com/interactive/2018/10/07/climate/ipcc-report-half-degree.html

700   Berardelli, Jeff. "How Climate Change Is Making Hurricanes More Dangerous » Yale Climate Connections." Yale Climate Connections, July 8, 2019. http://yaleclimateconnections.org/2019/07/how-climate-change-is-making-hurricanes-more-dangerous/

701   See Chapter 3 of this book.

702   Watts Up With That? "The Washington Post's Slander on Hurricanes and Climate Change," September 16, 2018. https://wattsupwiththat.com/2018/09/16/the-washington-posts-slander-on-hurricanes-and-climate-change/

703   Kumar, Larry, and Anthony Watts. "What You Need to Know and Are Not Told about Hurricanes." Watts Up With That?, September 15, 2017. https://wattsupwiththat.com/2017/09/15/what-you-need-to-know-and-are-not-told-about-hurricanes/

704   This is the first article on my computer relating to the Oregon Petition: https://en.wikipedia.org/wiki/Oregon_Petition

705   EurekAlert! "The Truth behind the Paris Agreement Climate Pledges," November 5, 2019. https://www.eurekalert.org/news-releases/914976

706   Beslik, Sasja. "5 Reasons Why the Paris Agreement Is a Joke (and How We Can Fix It)." Medium, April 7, 2019. https://medium.com/in-search-of-leverage/5-reasons-why-the-paris-agreement-is-a-joke-and-how-we-can-fix-it-4b636409bb05

707   Yachts to be exempt from EU's carbon pricing plan by Tyler Durden, Zero Hedge. 1/14/22 9:44 AM.

CHAPTER 8

708   Perry, Mark. "Michael Crichton Explains Why There Is 'No Such Thing as Consensus Science.'" American Enterprise Institute - AEI, December 15, 2019. https://www.aei.org/carpe-diem/ michael-crichton-explains-why-there-is-no-such-thing-as-consensus-science/

709   Prof. John Christy, the Distinguished Professor of Atmospheric Science and Director of the Earth System Science Center at The University of Alabama at Huntsville

710   Hourdin, Frédéric, Thorsten Mauritsen, Andrew Gettelman, Jean-Christophe Golaz, Venkatramani Balaji, Qingyun Duan, Doris Folini et al. "The art and science of climate model tuning." *Bulletin of the American Meteorological Society* 98, no. 3 (2017): 589-602.

711   In this chapter one degree refers to a Centigrade degree.

712   2015-2020

713   https://reefnation.com/can-coral-reefs-adapt-to-low-ph-conditions/

714   Ho, Leonard. "Lower pH Found to Slow Bacterial Coral Disease." Reefs.com, June 19, 2017. https://reefs. com/lower-ph-found-to-slow-bacterial-coral-disease/

715   Lehr, Jay. "Polar Bears: The End of a Climate Delusion Icon - CFACT." CFACT, January 22, 2020. https:// www.cfact.org/2020/01/22/polar-bears-the-end-of-a-climate-delusion-icon/

716   Grimes, David. "Good Thinking: Why flawed logic puts us all at risk," p. 311.

717   See the previous Chapter on the Paris Agreement and the Green New Deal. Mitchell, Travis. "U.S. Public Views on Climate and Energy." Pew Research Center Science & Society, November 25, 2019. https://www.pewresearch.org/ science/2019/11/25/u-s-public-views-on-climate-and-energy/

718   Bjørn Lomborg as reported in False Alarm.

719   Time. "Climate Change Doubled the Size of Forest Fires in Western U.S., Study Says," October 10, 2016. https://time.com/4525178/climate-change-forest-fires/

720   Brändlin, Anne Sophie. "Wildfires and Climate Change – DW – 06/19/2017." dw.com, 2017. https://www. dw.com/en/how-climate-change-is-increasing-forest-fires-around-the-world/a-19465490

721   Pohang University of Science & Technology (POSTECH). "Global Warming Is the Kindling That Caused Extensive Wildfire." Science Daly, 2020. https://www.sciencedaily.com/releases/2020/01/200110101029.htm

722   Lieberman, Bruce, and More by Bruce Lieberman. "Wildfires and Climate Change: What's the Connection? » Yale Climate Connections." Yale Climate Connections, July 2, 2019. http://yaleclimatecon-nections.org/2019/07/wildfires-and-climate-change-whats-the-connection/

723   Harrisson, Thomas. "Factcheck: How Global Warming Has Increased US Wildfires - Carbon Brief." Carbon Brief, August 9, 2018. https://www.carbonbrief.org/ factcheck-how-global-warming-has-increased-us-wildfires/

724   Ucsysa.org. "The Connection between climate change and wildfires." Updated 3/11/2020

725   Union of Concerned Scientists. "The Connection Between Climate Change and Wildfires," September 9, 2011. https://www.ucsusa.org/resources/climate-change-and-wildfires

726   Keeley, Jon E., and Alexandra D. Syphard. "Historical patterns of wildfire ignition sources in California ecosystems." *International Journal of Wildland Fire* 27, no. 12 (2018): 781-799. https://lpfw.org/wp-content/ uploads/2018/12/2018_Keeley-and-Syphard_Historical-patterns-of-wildfire-ignition-sources-in-California. pdf

727   Search for facts and information on wildfires. https://www.iii.org/fact-statistic/facts-statistics-wildfires

728   Daley, Jason. "Study Shows 84% of Wildfires Caused by Humans." Smithsonian Magazine, 2017. https:// www.smithsonianmag.com/smart-news/study-shows-84-wildfires-caused-humans-180962315/

729   Joyce, Christopher. "What's The Leading Cause Of Wildfires In The U.S.? Humans." NPR. org, February 27, 2017. https://www.npr.org/sections/thetwo-way/2017/02/27/517100594/ whats-the-leading-cause-of-wildfires-in-the-u-s-humans

730   Singleton, Laura . "90% of Wildland Fires Caused by Humans." White Mountain Independent, August 18, 2020. https://www.wmicentral.com/fire_season/90-of-wildland-fires-caused-by-humans/article_0aa779b8-a1c7-52bc-8b17-11f8b6200365.html

731   Search for facts and information on wildfires. https://www.iii.org/fact-statistic/facts-statistics-wildfires

732   "People Cause Most U.S. Wildfires," March 6, 2017. https://Earthobservatory.nasa.gov/images/89757/people-cause-most-us-.wildfires

733   NOAA Climate.gov. "If Carbon Dioxide Hits a New High Every Year, Why Isn't Every Year Hotter than the Last?," October 12, 2022. http://www.climate.gov/news-features/climate-qa/if-carbon-dioxide-hits-new-high-every-year-why-isn%E2%80%99t-every-year-hotter-last

734   Ibid.

735   Cranky Uncle by John Cook, p. 2.

736   See Chapter 1 for a more detailed discussion of CO_2

737   NY Times, 10/22/21, p. 1.

738   Grimes, David. "Good Thinking: Why flawed logic puts us all at risk," p. 311.

739   Burg, Natalie. "Who Funds the Fight Against Climate Change? - Means and Matters." Means and Matters, 2022. https://meansandmatters.bankofthewest.com/article/sustainable-living/taking-action/who-funds-the-fight-against-climate-change/

740   Gibbons, Michael T. "Higher Education R&D Increase of 3.3% in FY 2020 Is the Lowest since FY 2015 | NSF - National Science Foundation." Higher Education R&D Increase of 3.3% in FY 2020 Is the Lowest since FY 2015 | NSF - National Science Foundation, 2021. https://ncses.nsf.gov/pubs/nsf22312

741   Remarkably, some Climate Activist experts tell us that climate scientists are different than most people because they are not motivated financially by research grants. See Cranky Uncle vs. Climate Change, p. 137.

742   There are a few conservative colleges like Hillsdale College in Michigan which are exceptions.

743   The Guardian, May 18,2019.

744   Yiddish for Audacity

745   New York Time. "Global Warming Is Driving Polar Bears Toward Extinction, Researchers Say." https://www.nytimes.com/2020/07/20/climate/polar-bear-extinction.html

746   https://www.msn.com/en-us/news/technology/commentary-arctic-habitat-needs-to-be-saved-for-polar-bears/ar-BB1cPjDX

747   Voytko, Lisette. "Polar Bears Could Face Extinction By 2100 Due To Climate Change, Study Says." Forbes, July 20, 2020. https://www.forbes.com/sites/lisettevoytko/2020/07/20/polar-bears-could-face-extinction-by-2100-due-to-climate-change-study-says/

748   Aguilera, Jasmine. "'The Numbers Are Just Horrendous.' Almost 30,000 Species Face Extinction Because of Human Activity." Time, July 18, 2019. https://time.com/5629548/almost-30000-species-face-extinction-new-report/
The article does not point out any species killed off by global warming although it refers to several specific species like the Rhino Ray fish that are facing extinction because they have been over fished.

749   https://www.forbes.com/sites/trevornace/2020/02/24/70-90-percent-of-coral-reefs-will-disappear-over-the-next-20-years-scientists-say/We have seen how sun tan article forgets to mention these factors.
Gore, Al. An inconvenient truth: The crisis of global warming, p. 65. See Note 20 for more information. Lotions and copper from boats have been human causes of reef degradation, but the article forgets to mention these factors.

750   Buis, Alan. "How Climate Change May Be Impacting Storms Over Earth's Tropical Oceans – Climate Change: Vital Signs of the Planet." Climate Change: Vital Signs of the Planet, March 10, 2020. https://climate.nasa.gov/ask-nasa-climate/2956/how-climate-change-may-be-impacting-storms-over-earths-tropical-oceans/

751   The actual historic numbers indicate that we have had fewer hurricanes in most recent years. The climate activists suggest that we have had more Category 4 and Category 5 hurricanes, but even here there was less than one more large hurricane, and about 17 during the years between 1995 -2020.

752   Search for hurricane activity. https://www.google.com/search?q=hurricane+activity+2006+2015&ie=UTF-8&oe=UTF-8&hl=en-us&client=safari

753   Alexander, Ralph B. "Science Under Attack." Science Under Attack, July 15, 2019. https://www.scienceunderattack.com/blog/2019/7/15/no-evidence-that-climate-change-causes-weather-extremes-3-hurricanes-30

754   Contact any of the Realist sites mentioned in this chapter and a plethora of examples will be available.

755 Cornell University , Ithaca NY

756 Search on Americans who do not share their beliefs based on fear. https://www.cato.org/survey-reports/poll-62-americans-say-they-have-political-views-theyre-afraid-share

757 Ekins, Emily. "Most Americans Are Scared Stiff to Talk Politics. Why?" Cato Institute, 2020. https://www.cato.org/commentary/most-americans-are-scared-stiff-talk-politics-why

758 See Chapter I for an explanation.

759 Grumpy Uncle vs. Climate Change by John Cook, p. 59.

760 Ibid. p. 47

761 Also, it was not the Realists, but the Activists who told us in the 1970's that we were heading into an ice age. Also, I don't know any Realist who believes that 1998 was warmer than 2016.

762 Grumpy Uncle vs. Climate Change by John Cook, p 96.

763 Ibid. p. 98

764 Ibid. p. 44

765 Ibid. p. 44

766 Ibid.

767 John Cook in Grumpy Uncle Op. Cit.

CHAPTER 9

768 Caldwell, Christopher. "The Problem With Greta Thunberg's Climate Activism." New York Times. https://www.nytimes.com/2019/08/02/opinion/climate-change-greta-thunberg.html

769 Greta Thunberg, No one is too small to make a difference. pg. 30 (Kindle)

770 Ibid. pg. 10

771 Ibid. pg. 12

772 Ibid. pg. 96

773 Ibid. pg. 96

774 Ibid. pg. 96

775 Ibid. pg. 7

776 American Museum of Natural History. "Mass Extinction Events," 2022. https://www.amnh.org/exhibitions/dinosaurs-ancient-fossils/extinction/mass-extinction

777 Vanderbilt University. "Evidence That Earth's First Mass Extinction Was Caused by Critters, Not Catastrophe." https://news.vanderbilt.edu/2015/09/02/evidence-that-earths-first-mass-extinction-was-caused-by-critters-not-catastrophe/.

778 University of Ottawa. "The Secrets of Anticosti Island : New Discovery Sheds Light on Mass Extinction | About Us," May 21, 2018. https://www2.uottawa.ca/about-us/media/news/secrets-anticosti-island-new-discovery-sheds-light-mass-extinction

779 Katz, Cheryl. "New Theory for What Caused Earth's Second-Largest Mass Extinction." Animals, September 11, 2015. https://www.nationalgeographic.com/animals/article/15911-metals-extinction-ocean-oxygen-ordovician-silurian

780 Hickey, Hannah. "What Caused Earth's Biggest Mass Extinction?" Stanford Earth, 2018. https://earth.stanford.edu/news/what-caused-earths-biggest-mass-extinction

781 Weinbauer, Markus G., Benjamin Guinot, Christophe Migon, Francesca Malfatti, and Xavier Mari. "Skyfall—neglected roles of volcano ash and black carbon rich aerosols for microbial plankton in the ocean." *Journal of Plankton Research* 39, no. 2 (2017): 187-198. https://academic.oup.com/plankt/article/39/2/187/2966312

782 Search for information on volcanic ash. https://en.wikipedia.org/wiki/Volcanic_ash

783 Search for information and facts on volcanoes. https://www.google.com/search?q=wgat+solids+do+volcanoes+spew+out&ie=UTF-8&oe=UTF-8&hl=en-us&client=safari

784   National Geographic. "How the World's Deadliest Mass Extinction Actually Helped the Rise of Dinosaurs," September 11, 2020. https://www.nationalgeographic.com/science/article/how-the-worlds-worst-mass-extinction-set-the-stage-for-dinosaurs

785   Davis, Josh. "The Triassic Period: The Rise of the Dinosaurs." The Triassic Period: the rise of the dinosaurs | Natural History Museum. https://www.nhm.ac.uk/discover/the-triassic-period-the-rise-of-the-dinosaurs.html

786   Hickey, Hannah. "What Caused Earth's Biggest Mass Extinction?" Stanford Earth. https://earth.stanford.edu/news/what-caused-earths-biggest-mass-extinction.

787   American Museum of Natural History. "Mass Extinction Events," 2022. https://www.amnh.org/exhibitions/dinosaurs-ancient-fossils/extinction/mass-extinction

788   Ceballos, Gerardo, Paul R. Ehrlich, Anthony D. Barnosky, Andrés García, Robert M. Pringle, and Todd M. Palmer. "Accelerated modern human–induced species losses: Entering the sixth mass extinction." *Science advances* 1, no. 5 (2015): e1400253. https://advances.sciencemag.org/content/1/5/e1400253.full

789   Printed as Global Extinction Rates: Why Do Estimates Vary So Wildly? - Yale E360. The opinions are those of the International Union for the Conservation of Nature (IUCN).

790   Pierce, Fred. "Global Extinction Rates: Why Do Estimates Vary So Wildly?" Yale E360, 2015. https://e360.yale.edu/features/global_extinction_rates_why_do_estimates_vary_so_wildly

791   Ibid.

792   Robinson, Deena. "Sixth Mass Extinction of Wildlife Accelerating- Study | Earth.Org." Earth.Org, August 10, 2021. https://earth.org/sixth-mass-extinction-of-wildlife-accelerating/

793   Ibid.

794   Save The Rhino. "Saving the Sumatran Rhino | Save the Rhino International," May 17, 2019. https://www.savetherhino.org/asia/indonesia/working-together-to-save-the-sumatran-rhino/

795   Hsu, Jeremy. "The hard truth about the rhino horn "Aphrodisiac" market." *Scientific American, April* 5 (2017). https://www.scientificamerican.com/article/the-hard-truth-about-the-rhino-horn-aphrodisiac-market/

796   International Rhino Foundation. "Sumatran Rhino," September 29, 2020. https://rhinos.org/about-rhinos/rhino-species/sumatran-rhino/

797   Ibid.

798   Search for information and facts on the giant tortoise. Giant Tortoise | Species | WWF (worldwildlife.org)

799   Search for information and facts on the giant tortoise. https://en.wikipedia.org/wiki/Giant_tortoise

800   National Geographic. "Galápagos Tortoises, Facts and Photos." https://www.nationalgeographic.com/animals/reptiles/facts/galapagos-tortoise

801   Search for tortoise information and facts. Galápagos tortoise - Wikipedia

802   Harlequin Toads - Global Wildlife Conservation

803   Search for facts and information on the golden frog. https://www.google.com/search?q=chytrid+golden+frog+costa+rico&ie=UTF-8&oe=UTF-8&hl=en-us&client=safari

804   Sullivan, Kylie. "Presence and Preferred Thermal Range of Chytrid Fungus Pathogens in UCSC's Forest Ecology Research Plot (FERP)." University of California Santa Cruz, 2017. https://norriscenter.ucsc.edu/student-projects/smith-chytrid.pdf

805   Rainforest Trust. "Thirty Years After the Last Golden Toad Sighting, What Have We Learned? – Rainforest Trust," May 15, 2019. https://www.rainforesttrust.org/our-impact/rainforest-news/thirty-years-after-the-last-golden-toad-sighting-what-have-we-learned/
The species was declared "possibly extinct" in 2018, but a small population was discovered in 2020 in Ecuador.

806   Borrell, Brendan. "Is the Frog-Killing Chytrid Fungus Fueled by Climate Fluctuations?" Scientific American, 2009. https://www.scientificamerican.com/article/frog-killing-chytrid-fungus-climate-fluctuations/

807   Global Greenhouse Warming. "Extinction of Harlequin Frogs - Global Greenhouse Warming," July 19, 2012. http://www.global-greenhouse-warming.com/extinction-of-harlequin-frogs.html

808 Search for facts and information on the Harlequin poison frog. https://en.wikipedia.org/wiki/Harlequin_poison_frog

809 Lampo, Margarita, Celsa Señaris, and Carmen Zulay García. "Population dynamics of the critically endangered toad Atelopus cruciger and the fungal disease chytridiomycosis." *PloS one* 12, no. 6 (2017): e0179007. https://www.ncbi.nlm.nih.gov/pmc/articles/PMC5453621/

810 Sonn, Julia M., Ryan M. Utz, and Corinne L. Richards-Zawacki. "Effects of latitudinal, seasonal, and daily temperature variations on chytrid fungal infections in a North American frog." *Ecosphere* 10, no. 11 (2019): e02892. https://esajournals.onlinelibrary.wiley.com/doi/full/10.1002/ecs2.2892

811 Thunberg, Greta. *No one is too small to make a difference*. Penguin, 2019, p. 21.

812 NPR.org. "Transcript: Greta Thunberg's Speech At The U.N. Climate Action Summit," September 23, 2019. https://www.npr.org/2019/09/23/763452863/transcript-greta-thunbergs-speech-at-the-u-n-climate-action-summit

813 Thunberg, Greta. *No one is too small to make a difference*. Penguin, 2019 , p. 56.

814 Ibid. p. 106

815 German Advisory Council on Global Change. "Solving the Climate Dilemma: The Budget Approach," 2008. https://www.wbgu.de/fileadmin/user_upload/wbgu/publikationen/sondergutachten/sg2009/pdf/wbgu_sn2009_en.pdf

816 Dowson, George. "How Many Billion Tons of CO2 Have Humans Released into the Atmosphere from the Start of the Industrial Revolution until Now?" Quora. https://www.quora.com/How-many-billion-tons-of-CO2-have-humans-released-into-the-atmosphere-from-the-start-of-the-industrial-revolution-until-now

817 Thunberg, Greta. *No one is too small to make a difference*. Penguin, 2019. p. 76.

818 Ibid. p. 53-54

819 Ibid. p. 54

820 Thunberg, Greta. *No one is too small to make a difference*. Penguin, 2019. p. 1(Kindle).

821 United Nations. "Only 11 Years Left to Prevent Irreversible Damage from Climate Change, Speakers Warn during General Assembly High-Level Meeting," 2019. https://press.un.org/en/2019/ga12131.doc.htm

822 Ibid.

823 Thunberg, Greta. *No one is too small to make a difference*. Penguin, 2019. p. 56.

824 See Chapter 2

825 See Chapter 3

826 See Chapter 4 and earlier in this chapter.

827 Bastasch, Michael. "25 Years Of Predicting The Global Warming 'Tipping Point.'" 25 Years Of Predicting The Global Warming 'Tipping Point' | The Daily Caller, 2015. https://dailycaller.com/2015/05/04/25-years-of-predicting-the-global-warming-tipping-point/

828 United Nations. "Only 11 Years Left to Prevent Irreversible Damage from Climate Change, Speakers Warn during General Assembly High-Level Meeting," 2019. https://press.un.org/en/2019/ga12131.doc.htm All of the previous dates and quotes come from this source.

829 Sesno, Frank. "Opinion | The Positive Climate Tipping Point We Don't Talk About." YES! Magazine, January 1, 2022. https://www.yesmagazine.org/opinion/2021/04/23/climate-hope-positive-tipping-point

830 All of the predictions in this section came from Tipping Elements from a Global Perspective - University Press Scholarship

831 Thunberg, Greta. *No one is too small to make a difference*. Penguin, 2019, p. 10 (Kindle).

832 Ibid. p. 16

833 Ibid. p. 16

834 See Chapter 6

835 Ibid. p. 12-13

836 Ibid. p. 12-13

837 Ibid. p. 12-13

838   Arevalo, Alejandra . "Greta Thunberg's Net Worth: The Activist Is Worth More Than You Think - The List." The List, April 20, 2021. https://www.thelist.com/388507/greta-thunbergs-net-worth-the-activist-is-worth-more-than-you-think/

839   Relman, Eliza. "Alexandria Ocasio-Cortez Says Her Green New Deal Climate Plan Would Cost at Least $10 Trillion." Business Insider, 2019. https://www.businessinsider.com/alexandria-ocasio-cortez-says-green-new-deal-cost-10-trillion-2019-6

840   Kotkin, Joel. "Progressive California's growing race challenge," Orange County Register, June 30, 2018. https://www.ocregister.com/2018/06/30/progressive-californias-growing-race-challenge/

841   Thunberg, Greta. No one is too small to make a difference. Penguin, 2019, p. 22 (Kindle).

842   Search for information on speeches by Greta Thunberg. https://en.wikipedia.org/wiki/Speeches_of_Greta_Thunberg

843   Ibid.

844   Search for images of Jonathan Edwards. https://www.google.com/search?q=jonathan+edwards+picture&client=safari&hl=en-us&tbm=isch&source=iu&ictx=1&fir=j5D4-KQCQgWQbM%252CY4iUmU9gD5-27M%252C_&vet=1&usg=AI4_-kSfCcDx_DkmWPD2n8Y2q9iY4mKx8Q&sa=X&ved=2ahUKEwjDhuTE96XyAhWbKM0KHcgmD9UQ9QF6BAgNEAE&biw=1261&bih=898#imgrc=7-znl01i-LW8rM

845   Sinners in the Hands of an Angry God by Jonathan Edwards (blueletterbible.org). July 8, 1741. https://www.blueletterbible.org/Comm/edwards_jonathan/Sermons/Sinners.cfm

846   Search for information on Sinners in the Hands of an Angry God - Wikipedia. https://en.wikipedia.org/wiki/Sinners_in_the_Hands_of_an_Angry_God

847   "Jonathan Edwards Goes to Hell (House): Fear Appeals in American Evangelism." Source from "JSTOR. https://www.jstor.org/stable/20176759

848   Ibid.

849   Carrington, Damian. "Global Heating Warming up 'Nights Faster than Days.'" the Guardian, September 30, 2020. http://www.theguardian.com/environment/2020/oct/01/global-heating-warming-up-nights-faster-than-days

850   Pierre-Louis, Kendra, and Nadja Popovich. "Nights Are Warming Faster Than Days. Here's Why That's Dangerous. (Published 2018)." Nights Are Warming Faster Than Days. Here's Why That's Dangerous. - The New York Times, July 11, 2018. https://www.nytimes.com/interactive/2018/07/11/climate/summer-nights-warming-faster-than-days-dangerous.html

851   Knutson, Jacob. "Nights Are Warming Faster than Days in the U.S. Because of Climate Change." Axios, July 9, 2021. https://www.axios.com/2021/07/09/nights-warming-us-climate-change

852   Carrington, Damian. "Global Heating Warming up 'Nights Faster than Days.'" the Guardian, September 30, 2020. http://www.theguardian.com/environment/2020/oct/01/global-heating-warming-up-nights-faster-than-days
Pierre-Louis, Kendra, and Nadja Popovich. "Nights Are Warming Faster Than Days. Here's Why That's Dangerous. (Published 2018)." Nights Are Warming Faster Than Days. Here's Why That's Dangerous. - The New York Times, July 11, 2018. https://www.nytimes.com/interactive/2018/07/11/climate/summer-nights-warming-faster-than-days-dangerous.html

853   Mudambi, Veer. "Let It Snow?" Worcester Magazine, 2022. https://www.worcestermag.com/story/lifestyle/2022/01/13/let-snow-winters-new-england-getting-warmer-what-does-mean/9128528002/

854   Ibid.

855   Thunberg, Greta. No one is too small to make a difference. Penguin, 2019, p. 96 (Kindle).

856   Ibid. p. 96

857   Ibid. p. 9

858   Ibid. p. 66

859   Ibid.

860   Search for information on Climate Change and Mental Health Connections (psychiatry.org). https://www.psychiatry.org/patients-families/climate-change-and-mental-health-connections

861   Search for information on Climate Change and Mental Health Connections (psychiatry.org). https://www.psychiatry.org/patients-families/climate-change-and-mental-health-connections

862   Ibid.

863   ibid.

864   See Chapter 2

865   https://yaleclimateconnections.org/2020/02/how-climate-change-affects-mental-health/ Yale School of the Environment

866   Farmer, Sam. "How Greta Thunberg's Autism Helped Make Her the World's Most Important Person for 2020." Changing America. Accessed November 21, 2022. https://thehill.com/changing-america/well-being/468091-opinion-activist-greta-thunbergs-autism-doesnt-hold-her-back/

867   The Independent. "Greta Thunberg Was Depressed and Refusing to Eat Years before Climate Strike, Father Reveals," December 30, 2019. https://www.independent.co.uk/life-style/greta-thunberg-depression-father-svante-radio-4-today-climate-protest-a9263936.html.

868   Author quotes. https://www.goodreads.com/author/quotes/8088.Carlos_Castaneda

869   Search for author quotes. https://www.goodreads.com/quotes/6946116-success-in-life-could-be-defined-as-the-continued-expansion

870   See the previous Chapter on the Paris Agreement and the Green New Deal.

871   Search for quotes. https://www.goodreads.com/quotes/7077077-a-thing-of-beauty-is-a-joy-for-ever-its

872   Chopra, Deepak. *The Seven Spiritual Laws of Success-One Hour of Wisdom: A Pocketbook Guide to Fulfilling Your Dreams*. Amber-Allen Publishing, 2010.

873   If you want to worry about something, then worry about things that are important which we can do something about, like how we can improve the education of our children, our ability to encourage more self-responsibility and our ability to discuss difficult subjects, with respect and without emotion, with others who disagree with us.

INDEX

Notes